ON WINGS OF CHEER

ON WINGS
OF CHEER

A Red-Winged Blackbird Shares
His Happy Heart

by

SAM CAMPBELL
The Philosopher of the Forest

A.B. Publishing, Inc.
Ithaca MI

Cover Artist:
James Converse

Cover Designer:
Chrystique Neibauer

Printed in the United States of America

Published by:
A. B. Publishing, Inc.
Ithaca, MI 48847
www.abpub.com

To the Wilderness World

CONTENTS

ON WINGS OF CHEER

I

A BIRD IN THE HAND

As I SAT at my semicircular desk before the wide windows in our northwoods cabin, a startling realization dawned on me. I had spring fever! There was no sense in it, for this was the fall season. Nevertheless the symptoms were unmistakable. About me were piled mounds of papers representing work partly done or waiting to be done. I paid no attention to it, but sat staring idly out over the lake, now sparkling as if strewn with diamonds. In my typewriter was inserted a much neglected sheet of paper on which had been written "Page one"—hours ago, and nothing added to it. I stared past this, too, and watched the flight of an oak leaf as it left a tree and fluttered slowly to earth, hesitating as if it were selecting a comfortable spot in which to spend the winter.

I couldn't blame myself entirely. It was a strange autumn. There were few of the foretastes of cold weather we expect at this season in the north country. Soft breezes designed for May and June brought unseasonable warmth as though Nature had someway skipped winter and by short cut had entered another spring. The carnival of autumn reached its colorful climax amid temperatures that brought new bloom to some summer flowers. The flaring red of maple leaves, the maroon of oaks, the golden yellow of aspens fairly flamed against azure skies. Birds were puzzled too. Migrants forgot their travel plans.

Feathered crooners broke out with serenades designed for mating season. We heard the full song of the white-throated sparrow, the complete aria of the purple finch, and the murmuring melodies of Brewer's blackbirds and tree sparrows. From high in the blue skies came the cries of ravens and crows, sounding like the laughing of Nature itself at the tricks she was playing with her seasons.

Giny contributed greatly to my malady. She had chosen this hour to bake cookies—the same kind she had made that wonderful day in May when we had returned to our Sanctuary. Their aroma drifted to me, lulling my drowsy senses pleasantly.

Hi-Bub added his part also. He was just outside the cabin door, playing with chipmunks, squirrels, blue jays, nuthatches, chickadees and the many other birds that came to his feet to accept the food he offered them. I listened to his endless chatter, mingled with the happy voices of his wildwood guests.

"Blooey, you're a thwell bird!" said the lad. "Come on, here-th a peanut. No, not you, Th-tubby," he directed a reprimand to our ambitious chipmunk. "Thith one ith for Blooey. Oh—I didn't mean to thcare you. Here-th one for you. Don't bite my finger. That-th no peanut. Quick! Run! Here come-th Th-till-Mo. Hurry!"

There was a wild flurry among the feeding creatures as our dynamic red squirrel entered the circle like a whirl-wind. Stubby the chipmunk scampered for his under-ground home. Blue jays rose to the safety of trees. Other birds headed for distant points.

"Now lookut what you do!" cried Hi-Bub, who was

always trying to make peace between the conflicting species. "Th-till-Mo, do you have to chaith everything? Couldn't you walk? All right, here-th a peanut—but after thith be nith."

Still-Mo, the old red squirrel who had lived with us for several years, apparently took the peanut and scampered away. Other creatures returned as the disturbing element disappeared from the scene. The feeding went on, and so did Hi-Bub's chatter. It was just the kind of thing that fitted my mood. I could listen in with no effort. It demanded nothing of me.

Hi-Bub was a boyish boy now living at those wonderful years that are a blending of bud and blossom. Childhood was still evident in fat hands, plump cheeks, a delightful lisp and a self-inflammatory imagination. Yet manhood was peering through—in his eyes, his mannerisms, his questions, and in his character.

I fell to thinking about him. It was easy to do, for I love him so much. He is not our son, though he could not mean more to us if he were. His love of Nature had paved the way for our companionship. His home was in a village some miles away where he attended school. Because of his intense interest in our animals and the Sanctuary, his parents "lent" him to us each Saturday and Sunday. I had the conviction that the rest of the week was just a period of waiting for these days in the forest, as far as he was concerned. Right in the midst of this meditation, I was startled by his voice calling me in great excitement.

"Tham Cammel! Tham Cammel! Come quick. Come quick!"

I went quickly. There was a quality in his cry that frightened me. I thought at least a tree must have fallen on him. Papers I had so carefully arranged went fluttering to the floor in disorder. Books flew to the far corners of the cabin as I dashed out the front door to cause another scene of wild confusion there. A score of birds rose with a flurry of wings that blew autumn leaves hither and yon. Stubby and all the other diners raced for points of safety. In a second the feeding station was cleared of its customers, and there sat Hi-Bub looking up at me as calm as you please, not the victim of a tree falling or any other kind of calamity.

"Oh, oh—you thcared 'im!" he exclaimed.

"You mean frightened—frightened is the better word," I said. My spring fever had vanished under the effect of excitement. "What or whom did I frighten?"

"Oh, yeth," agreed the boy, "I forgot. I mean frighten. He wuth here, he wuth right here, and you thcared him."

"Frightened."

"Yeth."

"But, Hi-Bub, tell me, whom did I scare—I mean frighten? I heard you call and I nearly knocked the side out of the cabin to get to you. Now here you are with nothing wrong. What was the matter? Who was here?"

"It wuth him, all right," insisted the boy.

"It was he."

"Yeth, that-th what I thaid, it wuth him."

"He!"

"Yeth."

"All right, let's overlook the grammar—who was here and whom did I scare?"

"It wuth Cheer," said the boy, with enthusiasm. "Cheer wuth right here an' I thaw him!" He pointed with a crooked little finger to a balsam tree very close at hand.

I drew a deep breath and looked at the lad with tolerant amusement. He was such an adept at tall stories of his own concoction it was difficult to know what to believe. Cheer, the red-winged blackbird, had been one of the grand surprises of the summer. The sleek creature had taken to us in a manner that amazed and delighted us. He appeared one day at the feeding station and immediately made himself perfectly at home. From the start he had no fear of us. The first day we saw him he hopped up to my feet and took a bit of crumbled peanut I had placed on the toe of my shoe. From then on each day saw an unfolding of friendship with this lovely bird. In less than a week he was feeding from our hands. His happy call sounded so much like the word "Cheer" that we gave him that name.

"But, Hi-Bub," I said, always hoping to develop in our young friend that accuracy of thought and statement so vital to good nature study, "Cheer has been gone a long time. Remember, I told you he flew away with a flock of his own kind? He has gone a long distance by now. I feel sure you didn't see him."

"Why, Tham Cammel." There was a bit of reprimand in the lad's voice. "I thaw 'im. He wuth right here. You thcared 'im."

"Frightened."

"Yeth."

I saw I couldn't argue him out of it. He believed he had seen Cheer. Perhaps it was one of the other blackbirds, I thought. Perhaps it was a shadow. At any rate it wasn't important, so I returned to the cabin to clean up the mess of papers, requesting Hi-Bub to let me know if he saw the famous redwing again.

"I'll call if he come-th," he said.

"Well—not the way you did before," I cautioned. "Just whisper this time."

"Tho I don't thcare 'im."

"Frighten."

"Yeth."

I returned in search of my spring fever. It wasn't hard to find. The sun streamed through trees largely shorn of their leaves. The breeze bore a sweet savor born of balsam and basswood trees. I fingered the papers, hoping to get down to work, but just about as aimlessly as before, when suddenly I heard a call that is difficult to describe. If a punctured automobile tire were able to attempt my name with its last escaping breath, the sound would be somewhat similar.

"Tham Cammel!" came the exaggerated whisper from outside the front door. "Tham Cammel!"

The call was meant for me, but it affected the entire community. Giny heard it and came in from her cooky baking. Birds, chipmunks and squirrels heard it too, and once more departed for distant points. I went to the door to find Hi-Bub coughing from his efforts at a super-whisper.

"I thcared 'im," he said, and cleared his throat. "He wuth here and I thcared 'im."

I evaded grammatical comment.

"Are you sure you saw a red-winged blackbird?" I asked.

"Or was it just a 'maginary?" put in Giny, offering Hi-Bub a way out.

"It wuth Cheer!" he said emphatically. "He wuth here." He indicated the same balsam as before. Hi-Bub seemed a bit hurt at our doubts. It was not wise to question him further.

"Well, I'll tell you what to do," I said. "If he comes again, don't call or whisper—sing. Keep your voice low and even, and we will hear you. If Cheer is here, we've given him a bad reception."

All right, agreed Hi-Bub, he would sing. And it wasn't long before he did. His unending talk to the various creatures who now came back took on the character of a chant. One moment I heard him trying to settle differences among his customers; the next there was a drone that bore some similarity to "America the Beautiful."

"Oh, Tham Cammel, he'th here—Tham Cammel, he'th here—he'th in thith little tree. Tham Cammel, he'th here—Tham Cammel, he'th here—he'th comin' up to my hand. Hello, Cheer, hello, Cheer—now don't be thcared— oh, I mean frightened. . . ."

Giny and I had tiptoed to the door. There on the

ground, at the finger tips of Hi-Bub's proffered **hand** stood the beautiful bird that had given us so much joy in weeks past. He was taking bits of grain and peanuts. Even as we watched, breathless in our joy, the creature puffed up in blackbird style and uttered his happy "Cheer, Cheer."

Restraining our impulse to rush to him, we advanced slowly from the door, talking to him in the calmest voices we could muster. His confidence was restored **by** this more quiet reception, and the bird gave evidence of his own joy at the reunion. He flew to a branch in a white pine, a perch that had been his favorite during the summer. Here he went through his routine of cute little movements that definitely resembled a dance. He strutted back and forth, bending his beak close to his feet as if watching each step. Then he spread his wings, to reveal fully the beauty of his brilliant coloring. He called his squeaky "Cheer, Cheer," and added to it the mating song often described as "Congare-e-e-e-e-e."

I do not want to draw comparisons between the many wild creatures that have given us their friendship at our northwoods Sanctuary. Each one has his peculiar charm and appeal. There was Inky the porcupine, so homely and awkward, yet so full of devotion and loyalty to us that his name became a symbol of friendship. There were the two porcupines we named Salt and Pepper, and surely their friendship left us forever in their debt. Halitosis, our friendly skunk, gave us a companionship of sweeter savor than the reputation of his kind would suggest. The bears, raccoons, woodchucks, deer and other creatures that responded to our kindness all carved a special place in our hearts. Cheer was but one more in the long list. He made his own niche in our affections. He was what his name suggested—a messenger of the sheer joy of life.

"Why do you suppose he has come back?" Giny was asking. "There are no others of his kind left, and winter is almost here. What would make him return at this late day?"

"Why, Mithuth Cammel, don't you know?" asked Hi-Bub in surprise.

"Well—I'm not sure."

Hi-Bub swallowed hard, and then looked up, giving in

his answer the cause of all things good and worth while in life. "Why," he said, his eyes widening, "why—he love-th you!"

The next morning Cheer was at our bedroom window in the first gray light of dawn. He called Hi-Bub, too, out in the small cabin which had been assigned to our boy guest as his very own. There was no more time for spring fever, even though the warm autumn weather persisted—not with that little feathered bundle of good cheer around. We composed a poem to Cheer that day, which ran as follows:

> Fly above your troubles,
> They are only bubbles.
> 　Cheer, cheer, cheer.
>
> There's a strength to gladness
> That will conquer sadness.
> 　Cheer, cheer, cheer.
>
> Let your heart keep singing,
> Let your faith keep winging,
> Into life keep bringing
> 　Cheer, cheer, cheer.

However, I liked best Hi-Bub's remark as this week end came to a close and he was about to leave for home. He looked down at the blackbird who was then at his very feet. The boy's eyes glowed and he seemed to smile from head to toes as he said simply, "You're a thwell bird, Cheer!"

II

ANIMAL WORLD AND HI-BUB

IT WAS Saturday morning and I had no need of consulting a calendar to convince me of this fact. Life in the forest has made me somewhat careless with the names of days. When I have dwelt for a period in the realm of plants, animals, landscapes and endless evolution I get the Mondays, Tuesdays, Wednesdays and such things rather badly mixed. After all, Nature has only one day and one night. The idea of having a lot of different kinds of days is a purely human notion.

But Saturday had its unmistakable marks of distinction at the Sanctuary that autumn. Dawn had advanced but little when out in the misty distance across our lake we heard the squeak of an oarlock. We knew the sound very well for we had heard it often before—on Saturdays. Hi-Bub was coming! At the end of the road a boat had been left for his convenience, for our cabin is on an island. His patient, devoted father rose early to bring his little budding naturalist to us for this all-important, regular week-end visit.

"Hello-o-o-o-o, Tham Cammel!" called the expected boyish voice across the still waters.

"Hello-o-o-o-o, Hi-Bub," Giny and I called back in unison as we went to meet the boat.

"Thith ith Thaturday, do you know ut?" he called, his voice breaking under the difficulty of lisping and shouting at the same time.

"What, Hi-Bub—what did you say?" I asked, just wanting to hear him lisp again.

"Thith ith Thaturday—Thaturday! Here I come!" He sounded as if he wouldn't even wait for the boat.

"Come on, Hi-Bub," called Giny. "We're waiting for you and we have lots to do. Hurry! Hurry!"

"Daddy," we heard him say in lower voice, "can't you go fathter?"

"Take it easy, son," came the deep voice of the father. "That island won't get away from you. Careful—don't fall overboard."

The oars dipped and dipped, and the oarlock squeaked until finally they reached our shore.

"Thought he would never get through this week," commented the daddy as he guided the boat to the landing. "It seems that there's some bird out here by the name of Cheer who will never get anything to eat or drink unless a certain boy gives it to him."

"Ith he here, Tham Cammel?" broke in Hi-Bub, stumbling, crawling and scrambling his way ashore. "Ith he here? Ith Cheer here? Ith——"

"Yes, yes, Hi-Bub—he is here," laughed Giny. "He's been at the feeding station every day, and I'm sure he has been looking for you."

"Oh boy, oh boy, oh boy!" exclaimed the excited youngster. "Lookut! Lookut what I got." He held up a well-filled paper bag. "It-th cooky crumbth for Cheer. Mom thaid I could bring 'em."

"Yes," commented his daddy, with a wink and a smile. "Mom said he could bring the crumbs from the cooky jar. I never knew cookies had so many crumbs. I think maybe some very sound cookies were crushed up into crumbs just so that bag would be full."

"Such things happen when boy meets bird," I agreed, studying the beaming Hi-Bub accusingly. "But how about some breakfast?"

"Thanks—but we ate while it was still dark." The father handed a little overnight bag to us. "Now that I have the all-important job done I must go to my work. Good-by, you little rascal," he added to Hi-Bub, and brought his huge fist menacingly against the boy's chin. "Remember what your mother told you. I'll pick you up tomorrow afternoon and take you home."

"Until another Thaturday—huh?" put in Hi-Bub, working far ahead.

"O.K.—unless the Campbells get tired of you. Now good-by and have fun."

"Oh, Tham Cammel duthn't get tired," insisted Hi-Bub quickly. "You thee, he can retht all week after I'm gone."

"I expect it takes just that," said the daddy, though Hi-Bub missed the significance of the remark.

The animals of our Sanctuary soon knew it was Saturday too. News does get around among these forest folk.

Cheer came up in his merriest mood. The cooky crumbs went over in a big way. We heard Hi-Bub's soft laugh mingled with the joyous twittering and calling of the redwing. Chipmunks, squirrels and birds of many varieties gathered about the happy lad until he was the center of what resembled a three-ringed circus concentrated into one.

To Hi-Bub these creatures were people. He talked to them just as he did to us, fully believing that he was understood. Confidentially he told Stubby the chipmunk of little problems in school. Cheer was informed that "Daddy got me a new pair of shoeth." Apparently he received answers beyond the reach of my ears. "Where wuth you, Cheer, when you wuth gone tho long?" I heard him ask as the redwing ate crumbs from his hand. "Oh, wuth you?" he added after receiving some silent reply. "Did you have fun?" Obviously Cheer had fun wherever he went and whatever he did, for Hi-Bub closed this conversation with "Well, well—that-th nith. I'm glad."

We knew Hi-Bub first in a large city many miles away. When we met him there at a school, he was already familiar with many of our friendly animals through the stories his parents had read to him from my books.

"Hard to believe that is the same tyke we saw living back among those tall buildings and hard-paved streets," Giny said as we watched him through the window. "He takes to the woods as naturally as the animals themselves."

Later in the day I managed to listen in on a conversation between Hi-Bub and Still-Mo the red squirrel. Outside the cabin an unaccustomed silence reigned, and I

went searching for the cause of it. I discovered Hi-Bub
sitting on the ground, looking up at Still-Mo who was
perched on a stump. Probably the squirrel was quite
fatigued from the hectic Saturday activities and needed
a bit of rest. Hi-Bub was talking and I didn't count it
eavesdropping to stand within hearing distance.

"I wuth thcolded yethterday, Th-till-Mo," said the
little lad meditatively.

Still-Mo stared straight ahead.

"I wuth bad, I gueth," went on the boy. "But I didn't
mean to be."

The squirrel remained silent.

"You thee, I wuth helpin' Mother," Hi-Bub explained with extreme seriousness. "I wuth helpin' to bring Daddy thome pumpkin pie at dinner. I like pumpkin pie. Do you like pumpkin pie, Th-till-Mo?" There was a moment's pause, and then the boy added, "Uh-huh, I thought you did. Well, Mother cut the pie in the kitchen," he went on, moving a bit closer to his diminutive audience. Then in utmost confidence of the animal's interest and understanding, Hi-Bub told the stoical Still-Mo how there had been three pieces of pie on as many plates. His job was to transport this dessert into the dining room. Parental instructions were that he should take one plate at a time, as that was enough for a boy his size to handle properly. Hi-Bub was seized with the idea of efficiency. Hence he came prancing through the dining-room door with a portion of pie in each hand.

His daddy looked up horrified, though Still-Mo was told that "Daddy wuth thcared." "Look out, son," the father had exclaimed. "In your left hand—that piece is slipping off the plate!" Hi-Bub looked. Sure enough the plate in the left hand was sloping and the pie creeping toward calamity. Hastily he leveled the plate, but he only transferred the spot of disaster. The plate in his right hand now dipped to a dangerous angle. The piece of pie it contained, obedient to the law of gravity and unmindful of the cries of mother and father, slid off the plate and landed upside down on the floor to the tune of an impressive *plop*.

"An' what do you think, Th-till-Mo?" the boy continued, while the squirrel scratched violently at some unexplained itch. "When I looked to see what had happened, the other pieth of pie went *plop* on the floor too."

Hi-Bub looked rather sadly at the ground, recalling details of the disaster, while Still-Mo eyed a chipmunk that passed near by, likely wishing such things had never been created.

"It wuth an awful meth, Th-till-Mo," Hi-Bub went on. "I wuth thcolded becauth I didn't mind."

Still-Mo had been quiet long enough, however. Uttering a little chirp, she now ran away on some errand of her own. Perhaps she left for the same purpose I did—so I could find a secluded spot in which to indulge the laugh I didn't want Hi-Bub to hear.

Our lad was ready for bed early this Saturday evening. It had been a wonderful day, and he had squeezed from it every drop of experience possible. Now he was tired. Giny and I took him to his cabin and tucked him in. The forest night, filled with mystery and miracle, reigned. For a few minutes there was a great tug of war going on in Hi-Bub's thoughts. Sleep was calling him. Yet there were other voices too. We heard our raccoons, Rack, Ruin and Racket, come to get the food we had placed outside for them. We had to lift Hi-Bub from his bed and hold him up to look through a window at these lovely nocturnal creatures, centered in a spotlight. Then there was another sound that banished the idea of sleep temporarily, and caused the 'coons to lift their heads in alertness. From deep in the forest came the high-pitched cries of coyotes.

"O-o-o-o-o," said Hi-Bub. He was a little apprehensive in spite of himself.

"Remember what we have told you, Hi-Bub," said Giny as we took him back to his bed. "There is nothing in all the woods that will hurt you."

"Yeth, I know," agreed the boy. "I wuth wonderin' if they like cooky crumbth."

"Listen!" I cautioned. "There's another voice. Do you recognize it?"

We all identified the deep mournful cry of a great timber wolf. It gladdened our hearts to hear it. These creatures, so little understood by mankind, have been disappearing from the north country. Rarely now is their weird call heard, though it is needed to complete the symphony of the wilderness.

"He thingth nith," said Hi-Bub. "Could we thee him thometime?"

It wasn't likely that we would. Through the autumn we had been thrilled by his occasional call, always coming from the same point out in the night. But to see such a creature is an adventure not to be anticipated, for he is the shyest of the shy.

We had named our unseen friend "Mephistopheles" because of his enticing bass voice. Poor Hi-Bub once started into that word and nearly choked before he got out at the other end. Hence we shortened it to "Meph"— and even that is tough enough for a fellow who lisps.

There was silence now, and Giny and I looked down at Hi-Bub as his eyes tried to close.

"Tham Cammel," he said from somewhere on the border of dreamland.

"Yes, Hi-Bub?"

"Ith Cheer going to fly away thoon?"

"Why, yes, old top—I expect Cheer will fly south any time now," I replied. "He couldn't live here in the winter, you know. He will fly to join his brothers and sisters. You see, he just stayed to play with you. All the other blackbirds left long ago. Isn't he nice to stay?"

Yes, Cheer was nice to do that. There were more questions, however, coming from a mind that obviously had been dwelling on the subject.

"Will Th-tubby and Beggar Boy go away?"

"No, they do not go away. They will go down in those holes in the ground you have seen them enter. There they've stored the peanuts you gave them, along with seeds, acorns, grain and such things for winter food. They will sleep till spring, just the way woodchucks do."

"Will Racket go 'way?" he persisted.

"No, the pretty raccoon will live back in the woods somewhere in a hollow tree. She sleeps most of the winter, but awakens occasionally to eat."

"Will Th-till-Mo go 'way?"

"No, Still-Mo will stay right here. She will eat the food you have given her, and she doesn't sleep like the raccoon."

Hi-Bub was very quiet. His big eyes avoided mine and looked at the ceiling of the cabin. Something was making him serious to the point of being heavy.

"Tham Cammel," he said again.

"Yes, Hi-Bub."

"Are you and Mithuth Cammel going 'way?"

There was the catch, and I had felt it. We had all been avoiding this subject. Now it was coming out. I squeezed Hi-Bub's hands in mine. "Yes, my little man, my fine naturalist—we are going away. In a short time we will pack up and leave. We must be gone all winter. You ..."

I hesitated. His lower lip was trembling.

"Why, Hi-Bub, you aren't going to feel that way, are you? Giny and I have to go."

"Why?" He had no breath to say more.

"Because we must give lectures to lots of audiences. We want to show them pictures of our animals and tell them how beautiful it is here. You want us to do that, don't you?"

Hi-Bub wasn't so sure, and he said so with silence.

"You remember, don't you, Hi-Bub, when we came to your school in the big city?" I went on. "You remember how happy it made you to see the pictures. Don't you think we should try to make others happy that way too?"

There was a slight nod of the head accompanied by a sniff, while one tear got away and crept down his cheek. It is hard to know what to do or say at a time like that, especially when there were tears of my own so close to the surface that if I said the wrong thing I would release them.

"Hi-Bub," I said, after a trying interval.

"Yeth, Tham Cammel."

"What do you suppose our red-winged blackbird will

say when he starts away on his long journey? He doesn't want to go either. He has stayed a long time to prove that. But he will go someday, and what do you think he will say?"

There was a moment's hesitation while several sniffs adjusted some feelings and a plump little hand rubbed away overanxious tears. Finally his heroic attempt at a smile succeeded, and he said strongly, "Cheer! Cheer! Cheer!"

III

OLD CHARLEY, THE GRINNING GREMLIN

Hi-Bub's sadness at our impending departure was sharply interrupted the next week. Some new business came to hand that left him no time to dwell on prospective loneliness. In fact, the entire community was suddenly stimulated with new life.

We were made a present of a live, snorting, five-hundred-pound black bear!

Bears are not novel in our forest. We have lots of them, and not infrequently we catch glimpses of one along our lake shore or on the trails. We have no complaint against them. In fact, the forest would lose something very precious if they were gone. They do not attack human beings. Normally they mind their own business and are so shy we count it a great experience when we see one.

The trouble with our gift bear was—he wasn't normal. He had been around human beings so much he had lost all fear of them. We heard of him first through a letter from a game farm where he had been raised. Old Charley, as they had named the bear, had been brought there when he was a cub. There he grew up, fed and cared for by human hands. He was a good bear, the letter said, though it was admitted that he had a "fiendish sense of humor." He liked nothing better than to frighten a new employee of the farm until he nearly jumped out of his shoes. While a keeper was washing out his cage, Old Charley bit the rubber hose in two and water squirted all over the man. Once he took the keeper's hat and sat on it, and refused to give it up until hours later. He enjoyed stealing his keeper's broom. In spite of his great size he wanted to play whenever anyone came near him. Seldom did any-one go into his cage without getting knocked down at least twice before leaving. Yet Old Charley was not cross. After each one of these stunts he would go over into a corner, and sit making a noise something like an out-board motor—which probably came from laughter down inside.

The problem was that Old Charley had outgrown his accommodations at the game farm. It was high time he was liberated in the forest. They asked permission to place him in the Sanctuary, where he would be safe from hunters. There the old bear could get accustomed to a wilder existence. In a few weeks he would enter hiber-nation. By spring, the letter stated, he would have for-gotten his domestic training and would be a normal bear.

Well, Old Charley arrived one October day. He was transported in a truck on which had been built a strong cage. He was taken back over a little fire lane that winds through the woods toward the more remote area of our Sanctuary.

Giny, Hi-Bub and I went along to see the bear re-leased. There was no question as to the joy of the great creature as the door of his cage was opened, and he jumped down on the forest floor. There was a noticeable sparkle in his eyes as he stood for a moment contemplating his surroundings. Here was the world as he remembered it in his earlier days. He sensed that he was at liberty. The trees fascinated him. He raced up to a large white pine and embraced it as if it were a long-lost friend. Then, snorting and puffing delightedly, he ran from one tree to another giving each the same affectionate greeting.

He seemed inclined to share his hugs with us when he discovered us in a little huddle a short distance away. He ran in our direction, but when he arrived at the spot we weren't there any more! I never saw people run faster. Hi-Bub's legs were simply a blur at the speed he went, though he was laughing and having the best of fun. "Come on, Tham Cammel," he called. I needed no urging. Neither did Giny, nor the men who had driven the truck from the game farm. Yet Old Charley didn't mean any harm. He hadn't the slightest intention of hurting anyone. He was happy and he wanted to play. But it is very difficult for a bear his size, with two-inch claws, to be gentle. We had no wish to have him wrap his arms about us and lick our faces, even if it were only an expression of love. We raced to the truck and soon were packed like sardines in the all-too-small cab.

Old Charley paid no more attention to us. He had had his fun. If we were sissies and didn't want to play, he still had plenty to amuse him. He boxed with bushes, rolled in tall grass, snorted and sniffed at everything, and finally disappeared on the run over a little hilltop.

"Oh boy, oh boy—that wuth the mothteth fun I ever had," declared the delighted Hi-Bub.

We went back to our cabin on the island. An adventure
had begun. Nothing like Old Charley had ever been
known in that country before. He took to the wilds
handily, but he never forgot what he had learned about
men. We tried to keep him near the point where he had
been liberated. There we established a feeding station
for him, and kept a good supply of his favorite foods at
hand. For several days he held to the region. We hid behind trees and watched him as he came up for his dinner.

Old Charley soon began pushing his horizons back.
This was too interesting a world for him to be contented
with one small part of it. Within a week he disappeared
and was gone for two days.

Then a story reached us of a huge bear that had been
seen several miles to the south of us along a forest road.
In fact, one man driving an automobile had got a very
good look at him. Seeing the fine-looking bear in the
brush at the side of the road, the man had stopped his car.
The bear promptly came right up to him "wearing a
smirk on his face and puffing like an outboard motor," the
man said. The windows of the car were hurriedly closed
and the driver sat there watching the fearless animal. To
his amazement the bear tried to get in the car. He pawed
at the doors and windows, he climbed up on the hood, and
then got up on top. Naturally those great bear claws left
numerous autographs in the paint. Once on the roof the
bear seemed contented and sat down. The driver was
virtually a prisoner in his own car, and not a very contented one either. The man didn't know what to do. He
could hear the bear as he moved about scratching himself.

Finally the great creature stretched out as if he intended to take a nap. Of course, the driver could have started up the car and run out from under the bear, but he had no wish to hurt the animal. Anyway, he had no assurance that as the bear fell off he wouldn't take half of the car with him. Presently he remembered some apples that were in the rear seat. He lowered a window slightly and dropped several of these on the ground. The bear promptly scrambled down, leaving more deep scratches in the paint and a dent in the hood as he went. The creature picked up an apple and began to down it in huge bites, while the driver scraped about an inch of rubber off his rear tires making a fast start down the highway.

"That must have been Old Charley," said Giny when the story was told us.

Hi-Bub giggled.

Old Charley showed up at his feeding station again and remained for several days. Then he disappeared. Soon another story reached us. This time it involved a cabin five miles to the north. The owners of the place had gone to town for supplies. A few rings of summer sausage had been left hanging on the back porch. When they returned the sausage was gone—and so was most of the porch. It was evident from large tracks in the sand that a bear had been there. Apparently he had caught the odor of that summer sausage. The scent of seasoned meat is just a cordial invitation to a bear to come on in and help himself. This bruin visitor had done just that. Getting into the porch was simple enough, for the screen door swung inward and no doubt gave way easily to his powerful paws. Getting the sausage was easy too, and from the grease spots on the floor it was clear that he had eaten the lunch right there. Then came the problem of getting out. The door had slammed behind him. It needed to be pulled open, and a bear knows nothing about pulling—only pushing. This creature must have pushed amazingly hard, for the door had gone outward whether the hinges were built that way or not—and with it went the entire frame and a section of the railing.

"It wuth Old Charley!" guessed Hi-Bub when this tale was told us.

Five miles southeast of us lived some people who had carved a little garden space out of the forest. Here they raised vegetables and some choice flowers. The only way they could protect their produce was to circle the plot of ground with an electric fence. This worked fairly well through the summer. Now that the autumn season was on, they were keeping the fence in operation until they could retrieve some very precious bulbs that were still in the ground. One evening they were startled to see a good-sized bear standing near the fence. They tapped on the window at him, but he showed not the least alarm and went about sniffing and investigating. They held their breath as the animal edged toward the electric fence. Their hearts all but stopped as he turned his nose away and began backing up toward the thing. Presently his short tail made the contact, and one hundred and twenty volts went racing all around under his black hide. Of all the indignities to heap on the king of the forest! The animal seemed paralyzed at first. Then he gave a snort and a leap that broke the contact. As if super-charged, he raced into the woods, breaking down bushes and small saplings as he went.

The people were doubled up with laughter, but their merriment suddenly ceased when they saw the bear coming back out of the forest. He wasn't running now, but was advancing with strides that reflected purpose and power. Straight to the fence he went. He sniffed at it with his nose. Again one hundred and twenty volts smote him, and he jumped back. Then with an angry growl he arose on his hind legs, front paws waving. The people looked at a spectacle of ferocity that made them vow they never would get in a boxing match with a bear. The animal struck the wire with his paw, and of course, was shocked anew. It infuriated him, and he lunged forward, breaking the fence and the electrical circuit. Free now of the mysterious power that had assailed him, the bear proceeded to tear that fence down, breaking the posts, not stopping until it was a tangled mass spread over the ground. Then extricating himself from the coils of wire, he raced into the woods.

Giny and I nodded our heads as we heard this story. "That's Charley," we said in unison.

There came the tale of the resort where the kitchen was surrounded with a screened porch. After the insect season was over, the door of this porch had been removed to make the carrying in of wood and supplies easier. A bear began to visit the place nightly and feast on scraps that were usually left in a bucket on the porch. The creature tried repeatedly to get into an icebox that stood near at hand. The cook grew afraid to go out on the porch, and something had to be done. One of the guests suggested that a big noise might frighten the animal away. Accordingly plans were made, and when the bear returned one night, all of a sudden there was the wildest pounding of dishpans and shouting! It worked perfectly. The bear was frightened until he nearly jumped out of his hide. The only trouble was that in his fear he lost memory of where the door was, and went right out through the side of the porch, taking nearly all of it with him.

That was Charley!

One day some men were doing road work a few miles to the east of the Sanctuary. They had driven to the point where the work was needed, and there at the roadside

parked their car. Their metal lunch boxes were left on the car seat—four of them. Road work is hard. The men shoveled and picked and chopped all through the morning hours. By noon they were ravenously hungry. Back to the car they trudged. "Man, am I anxious for that lunch today!" said one of them. "My wife baked an apple pie and I know she packed two pieces for me."

"There'll be mince pie for me," said another, "and that's my favorite."

"You can have your pie," said a third. "I'll take good old banana cake—there'll be some in my box today."

Then all four stopped talking and walking and just stared at the sight before them. Beside their automobile sat a huge bear having the time of his life. He had opened the car door and found the lunch boxes. A few scratches from his powerful paws had opened these and the tasty contents were spilled on the ground. In the midst of this picnic the bear was perched, making a noise like an outboard motor as he ate apple pie, mince pie, banana cake and sandwiches until his heart was content and his tummy too.

The men shouted, but the bear was not afraid. He had heard men shout before. They threw stones, but not very hard, for the car windows were close at hand. Helplessly the men had to stand there until their uninvited guest ate the last crumb of their lunches. Then with a snort or two of thanks, the great creature disappeared in the woods.

That was Charley!

A man and his wife came up for a quiet week end, the last of the season at their cabin in the pines by a neighboring lake. The first night was wonderful, all that they had expected it to be. But in the morning when they looked out the back door, there sat a big bear on the doorstep. He was looking in through the screen, and eying the icebox particularly. They shouted at him and stamped their feet, but he wouldn't move. They called him "pretty creature" and heaped compliments on him, but he was immune to flattery. There he sat, in perfect contentment, considering ways to get to that icebox.

At last the man of the house tossed an orange out a window. It interested the bear, and he ate it down skin and

all. But he didn't go away. He returned to the back step
and sat down. Another orange was tossed out. The bear
ate it, and then sat down on the back step. Seven oranges
were consumed this way, with the same result. Several
apples followed, then three loaves of bread and a dozen
sweet rolls. After eating all this, the animal apparently
figured there couldn't be anything left in the icebox, and
calmly walked away into the woods.

That was Charley!

Old Charley certainly got around. And wherever he
went he managed to get into trouble. There was danger
mixed in his adventures, though he seemed to lead a
charmed life. People who live in the woods won't let a
bear boss them around all the time. Upon several occasions rifles were leveled at him, and bullets fired that were
meant to bring his career to a close. Some way he escaped
them all, and lived on to get into more mischief.

Old Charley soon grew into an impish tradition. Like
the gremlins of the air forces he was the traditional source
of all trouble. When two of Giny's pies were forgotten
in the oven and burned to a crisp, it was Old Charley who
did it. When I was carrying an armload of wood in a
rainstorm and slipped and landed in a puddle—it was Old
Charley who tripped me. When Hi-Bub tipped over a
bottle of ink on his mother's tablecloth he said, "I gueth
it wuth Old Charley."

The community took up the tradition. The big black
bear became a prankish evil spirit who practiced sorcery.
His fiendish sense of humor feasted on trouble. One evening while driving I came to a truck that had slipped into

the ditch. Men were laboring to get it back on the road. "How did it happen?" I asked.

"Oh, just Old Charley," said one resignedly.

It was Old Charley who washed out the bridge over Pine River, planted mice in a neighbor's garret, broke a mooring line and set a launch adrift in an open lake, set off a forest fire, and even caused our autumn storms. All of which proves that a fellow had better be right careful about getting a bad reputation in this world, for folks are just looking for someone to blame for all their troubles.

The last time we saw Charley that autumn he was again near the place where he had been liberated. Giny, Hi-Bub and I found him at the foot of a little hill, much interested in the giant roots of a pine tree that had been overturned by the wind. Charley was raking leaves into the excavation made where the roots were pulled out of the soil. He had gathered cedar bark into this spot too. While he was not beginning his hibernation, he was preparing for it. We saw him roll about in the material he had collected, and then as if practicing his entry into his vast dreamland, he reached with his front paws and pulled leaves and bark over himself until he was buried. Then he arose, shook the dirt from his fur and went into the woods.

"That's Charley, all right," I whispered. "I wish for the good of the community he would go to sleep and that right away."

"He'th a *thwell* bear," whispered Hi-Bub.

IV

THE COMING OF LITTLE JOHN DEER FOOT

As the autumn advanced and the day of our departure neared, Giny and I discovered that Hi-Bub was not the only one whose thought was saddened at our leaving. For the first time in our experience we simply did not want to go. Our philosophy in the matter helped but little. We spoke of the joy we would have in meeting thousands of people and sharing with them the experiences and inspiration we had gathered in Nature. We knew the need people have for the wholesome influence of the forest, and that carrying our lectures to them was likely our best way of serving our fellow beings. Yet, when we finished all our arguments—we didn't want to go.

I strongly suspect that our state of mind was largely due to that youngster who visited us so regularly and faithfully. True, there were other factors. The unseasonable warmth continued. It was so much like springtime we felt we should be arriving instead of departing. The wilderness about us was teeming with interest and the promise of adventures. Old Charley the bear was an inexhaustible source of excitement. A host of memories and plans caught and tugged at us like the thorns of a blackberry thicket.

Still we might have dismissed all these things easily if

it hadn't been for leaving Hi-Bub. That smile of his, the sweet but strong character that looked out of his blue eyes, his infectious enthusiasm, his faith, his charming lisp—how were we to get along without them?

Here is where childhood is more resourceful than maturity. We grownups are handicapped by practical knowledge and a vague thing we call reality. Hi-Bub was free of such manacles. If he was to lose temporarily his friends of the forest, he knew just where and how to get another. This we learned on his last week-end visit before our departure.

It was a haunting autumn evening in which we sat before our final campfire. The air was just cool enough that the warmth of the flames was welcome. An unbelievably yellow moon slowly and silently ascended the heavens. Stars blinked their eyes in its strong light. Crickets droned their ancient melody. The lake looked like polished black marble, and the heavens lived again in its mirrored depths. Coyotes gave their weird cries to deepen the beauty and mystery of the night. Twice we heard the voice of Meph, the great timber wolf.

"Tham Cammel," said Hi-Bub, breaking a long period of silence.

"Yes."

"Did Indianth live in theth woodth?"

"Yes, Hi-Bub, Indians lived all through this country."

"Were they right here—right where we are now?"

"I feel sure they were. They traveled through these lakes in their birch-bark canoes, and no doubt sometimes they landed on this island."

"Well—" Hi-Bub was moved with a growing excitement—"well, do you thuppoth an Indian ever walked right here?" And he marched past the fire in strides that were overlong for such short legs.

"No doubt," I said, willing to agree to anything within the realm of possibility. "No doubt some great brave has walked right where you are walking now."

"Do you thuppoth he touched thith tree—here?" asked the boy, putting his hand against an ancient white pine which was now lighted by the glow of the fire.

"Well, Hi-Bub, that tree is probably one hundred and fifty years old and so it was here when Indians roamed this region. However, I think the exact spot a big brave would have touched is higher than you can reach."

"Oh-h-h-h!" exclaimed the boy, imagination aflame. "I thuppoth thith tree hath grown. Maybe the thpot he touched is way up there." He pointed to a place thirty feet from the ground.

Giny and I laughed. "No, Hi-Bub," I said, seeing a chance to teach him a nature fact. "A given point on a tree never grows higher. Trees put on new growth at the top, and they become larger around, but their sides do not creep upward. If you were to drive a nail in this tree, say four feet from the ground, twenty years from now that nail would still be at the same height. So if a great Indian brave landing here a hundred years ago touched this tree about here—" I indicated a spot on the bark about six feet up—"that same spot is there now."

With this explanation, nothing would do but that I must

lift Hi-Bub until he could place his hand on the spot our hypothetical Indian might have touched. Now the delighted youngster had walked where an Indian might have walked; he had stood where an Indian might have stood; and touched a tree where one day an Indian might have placed his hand. It was wonderful.

"Tham Cammel!" he said, his tones influenced by his enthusiasm. "Talk thome more—'bout Indianth."

"Well," I said as I carried him back to a seat between Giny and me, "I don't know very much about them, but I'll be glad to tell what I know. In this region lived Indians who were known as the Ojibwa. They were wise and clever people. They knew what plants in the woods to use as food. They raised maize, or Indian corn. North of here in a very large lake is an island on which they planted crops. When the first white men came to the region, they found the Indians farming that island. The Ojibwa were good hunters and fishermen, too. Can't you imagine even now their birch-bark canoes going along in the shadows near that distant shore?"

I never should have started that. Could he imagine that? He was way ahead of me. He had canoes so thick they were bumping into one another—"hunnerdth of 'em." The Indians were camped on those moonlit shores, they were gathering wild rice in the bays, they were singing, dancing, laughing about their campfire. "Don't you thuppoth there might be—just thum?" he insisted.

"No, Hi-Bub," I said laughing, "none of them is here now. It's fun though to know they were here, isn't it?"

Hi-Bub wasn't hearing me. His eyes were wide and lighted with excitement. "Did they have little boyth and girlth?" he asked, anxiously.

"Yes, surely they did."

"Did the boyth and girlth live right in theth very woodth?" he persisted.

"Yes, they played and learned Indian knowledge right in these very woods," I affirmed.

"M-m-m-m-m," went Hi-Bub, though I did not understand what was going on in his thought until later.

"Perhaps you would like to know about the grand old Indian chief who lives up here right now," I went on, while Hi-Bub looked up at me with both mouth and eyes wide open. "Well, he lives way back in that forest in the direction of the rising moon."

Then I related to the attentive youngster the story, as best I knew it, of an ancient and interesting character named John Shawano. Through the great forest to the east of us threads a road known as the Military Highway. This road follows rather accurately the very old Indian trail which connected Fort Howard (later Green Bay) on the shore of Lake Michigan with Ontonagon, Michigan, on Lake Superior. The last stands of big timber in the north country were along this roadway directly east of us. In the cathedral-like depths of that forest lived this strange character known to most people as just "Big John."

Each of the few times I had seen Big John Shawano I had been much impressed with his dignified bearing and startling appearance. He was known to be at least one hundred years old, possibly older. Yet he stood a full six feet four inches, straight as the pine trees among which he lived and just about as sturdy. His eyes were clear and steady. His bronze face showed no wrinkles, his hair was thick and dark. Few of the young woodsmen could keep pace with John on a hike through the woods. He thought nothing of swinging on his back a packsack bearing a hundred pounds of supplies and walking from town to his cabin twenty miles away.

No one ever succeeded in getting really confidential with Big John, or in drawing from him his priceless story. He was a legitimate chieftain though his tribe was long since scattered and gone. Yet he never surrendered the dignity of his office. On the wall of his small cabin hung a heavy war club. It had been carved by primitive knives from specially selected maple. A hard knot made a large knob at one end. The other end had a curved handle. Two eagle feathers were attached to the handle, a symbol that only a true chief might use. This war club had been given Big John by his father. He regarded it with pride. No one might borrow it or buy it, though some tried to do so. Few were permitted to handle it. Once he surprised me by saying, even though I fancied he scarcely knew me, "When John go on—you have him (the club). You kind to little brothers of woods. Where John go he no need war club. You have him then."

Big John believed wild animals were created for Indians. He hunted when he needed food. And yet he never harmed an animal needlessly and he wanted no one else to do so. He said, "Great Spirit give cow, pig, sheep to

white man. To Indian he give deer, porcupine, fish."
Game wardens of the region had a problem with Big
John, for he was convinced he had a divine right to hunt
whenever he needed food regardless of the laws white
men made.

When I stood in the presence of Big John I always had
the feeling that he came from another world. He lived in
dreams, traditions, legends. His kingdom was by no means
lost. In the sighing of the wind in the trees, the murmur
of running streams, the rumble of thunder, the soft breaking of wavelets against a shore line, he heard the voices
of his people. He said his tribe lived beyond the setting
sun, and someday he would go to them.

John Shawano was very proud of his ability as a woodsman. He could move about as silently as a shadow, as
swiftly as a fox. Many a party of hunters or fishermen
had been startled and not a little frightened to see suddenly standing before them this tall, powerful Indian.
Usually he would say not a word, but after looking at
them sternly for a moment would disappear into the forest.

Big John had the spirit of the pre-white-man Indian.
He kept aloof from some of the bad habits taken on by
fellow red men. He held to the legends of his race, and
fully believed that someday the Indians would take America back from the white men again. "Only," he said, "they
be good to white man. They treat him well."

Hi-Bub listened closely as I talked of Big John Shawano. It was past his bedtime and his eyes were heavy, but
his interest held. Presently he went to Giny, climbed into

her lap and rested his head on her shoulder. I thought the day was done for the young man, but not so.

"Tham Cammel," he said, his voice mellowed with sleepiness.

"Yes, Hi-Bub."

"Duth a little Indian boy live in the woodth?"

"Well, now . . ." I said hesitantly, not sure just what direction the conversation should take.

"Yeth, he duth," said Hi-Bub, blinking.

"He does?"

"Yeth, I know him."

I couldn't think what to say to that.

"He ith coming to play with me," went on the sleepy but inspired Hi-Bub.

"What is his name?" asked Giny, who is better at that sort of thing than I am.

"Little John Deer Foot," said Hi-Bub without hesitation.

"Big John and Little John—that sounds right," I put in.

"Where is Little John Deer Foot?" asked Giny.

It was apparent the conversation was about the equivalent of a bedtime story, for Hi-Bub was hovering along the border of dreamland. "He live-th in a beaverth houth," he said. His lisping was always more prominent when he was tired.

"When will you see him?" asked Giny, her cheek against his.

"Oh, he will come whenever I call him," said Hi-Bub, stirring himself for just a moment. "He will come to play with me. He ith going to keep me from being lonethome while you are gone."

There, I told you that childhood is more resourceful than adulthood. Our practical sense wouldn't let us have a 'maginary little boy to take along with us. But Hi-Bub could reach out beyond our dull senses and find a playmate who would stay with him and be satisfying. Lucky, blessed little Hi-Bub.

"And Little John Deer Foot will come to our Hi-Bub," Giny was crooning in his ear. "He will take you into the lodges of the beaver and into the woodchuck homes too. He will teach you to play on the otter's toboggan slide, and to ride on the wings of the eagle. Little John Deer Foot will teach you what the cricket is saying, the secret of sunset and dawn. He will join you in your dream, Hi-Bub, and no one can take him from you."

Somewhere in the middle of these sentences Hi-Bub had launched out into dreams. From the peaceful expression on his chubby face, they must have been lovely ones.

Giny and I—and Hi-Bub too, though he did not know it—sat by the campfire until it burned to white ashes. We must feast to our fill, for it would be many a moon before we would know such a scene again.

High overhead we heard the call of Canada geese in flight. Faintly we could see their V-shaped formation passing before the moon. They were heading south in response to a call in their hearts.

"Tomorrow we follow them," whispered Giny, for there was a call in our hearts too. And now that Hi-Bub had Little John Deer Foot, we no longer disliked going.

V

AUTUMN LEAVES

CHEER had us awake the next morning at dawn. It was well he did, for there was much to be done that day. As if he had known that, he flew to our bedroom window, perched on a convenient tree and called to us in a manner that left no doubt of his motive. He wanted us to get up. He went to Hi-Bub's window, too, and soon had the boy wide awake and in conversation with him.

What more pleasant manner of awakening could there be than to the musical notes of this blessed feathered alarm clock! His song and happy manners soon had us all laughing. Before we gave a thought to our own breakfast, we took his cherished peanut crumbs to him. He strutted about, hopped, talked and spread his gorgeous wings as he ate from our hands.

How much do animals know? How keen is their intuition and their understanding of circumstances? I am always stymied by these questions. There is the fear in answering them that we give creatures credit for either too much or too little intelligence. But certain it is that there is a character very deep and profound in these living things with which we share the world, and we glimpse a bit of their true nature only when our attitude is kindly, patient and anxious to understand.

Cheer was unusually persistent in his devotion that morning. In earlier days he would take a few bites of food from us, then as a rule fly away. Not on this autumn morning. He stayed right in our midst. If we walked away, he walked after us. He was reluctant to have us leave to eat our own breakfast, and perched in a tree near at hand where he could see us and sing to us. Food was left for him on the ground, but he did not want to be served that way. We must hold it for him. The companionship was as valuable as the crumbs themselves.

Now why this stepped-up display of affection? Did this little feathered mite know that we were leaving the Sanctuary that day? And did he know at that hour that he was leaving too? For so it happened. Before the day was done Cheer had sailed toward the ever-receding southern horizon—and we had too.

The north country sped its departing guests in a most effective way. We never let ourselves be deceived by a deviation from the usual pattern of that land. The north-woods is a rigorous place and it maintains its character. Our autumn had been disarmingly mild. Yet the disposition of the wilderness remained basically unchanged, and the region would not let us depart without convincing us of that fact.

We had packed our car and finished final closing errands at the cabin. Various kinds of food appropriate for our island pets were left out. The three of us went once more to Old Charley's feeding station, there to leave food that would last the bear until hibernation. We did not see him, though his great tracks were numerous.

During these operations Hi-Bub kept up a running conversation, one of those monotonous flows that one moment we wished would cease and the next we hoped would never end. He always lisped more when he was particularly excited. Now his characteristic was so persistent that Giny and I found ourselves lisping also!

Our lad was too much occupied to feel any sense of loneliness. A certain versatile and fabulous Little John Deer Foot was becoming very real to him. Already the long name had been shortened to "John." We frequently caught fragments of conversation between the two—at least we heard Hi-Bub's remarks and I presume if we had been a bit more attentive and imaginative we would have heard John's end of it.

"John—you keep pettin' Th-tubby while I go for more peanut-th," said Hi-Bub.

John must have done so, for when Hi-Bub returned Stubby the chipmunk was there patiently waiting for him. "Thankth, John," said Hi-Bub casually. "Now you go an' thee if Cheer ith all right. I think I heard him cry."

On inquiry I found that John had come back saying that Cheer was all right and would be over pretty soon. In a few minutes Cheer came, and you just can't argue against evidence like that!

Little John Deer Foot seemed to have no limitations. On Hi-Bub's instructions he went down in the woodchuck tunnels to see if Patty and O. Bologna were covered up well so they would be warm for winter. He went out to see if Rack and Ruin the raccoons had a good tree to live in. It seems that the tree wasn't so good—therefore Little

John Deer Foot guided them to another. The tireless Indian boy inspected the chipmunk homes and told the tiny striped creatures they had better store up more food. Strangely, that is just what they did. He told the squirrels to hide some food in the trees so it wouldn't be covered by snow—that was done too.

Hi-Bub was a relentless boss. He sent his invisible pal to pluck the last leaves off a birch tree. The leaves came floating down all right. He sent him back to say good-by to the coyotes and to old Meph, the wolf. Next he dispatched him to find Old Charley to tell the bear not to get into any more trouble but to go to bed early so he could wake up in the spring. I asked if Little John Deer Foot would please cover up our wood pile. I guess he was too

busy, for presently I saw that it hadn't been done and did it myself.

Toward noon came our parting pat from the north-woods. For a few minutes all nature stood perfectly still. In the northwestern sky we discovered some ominous, dark, low clouds. They were moving toward us at a startling pace, though about us the world was still calm. Not a breath of wind stirred, not a leaf moved, not a wave wrinkled the lake. As we arrived at the island on our re-turn from Old Charley's dining room, we could hear a roar in the distance. On faraway hills we could see trees bending and whipping about. The oncoming clouds were so low they seemed to brush the earth.

Suddenly the wind struck. Trees about the cabin seemed actually to bend before the gale came, as if they were try-ing to dodge the blow. In an instant it was cold. All memory of the mild autumn and summer temperatures was gone. Our thermometer recorded a drop of twenty degrees within as many minutes.

At the first touch of this wind we heard the call of Cheer. Rising gracefully and calling constantly, he dis-appeared over the treetops to the south. Some way we knew this was our last look at him, for this season at least. He took a portion of our hearts with him, and I am sure he left behind some of his. Skeptics may scoff at such things if they wish. They may say it was only the warm weather and the abundance of food that caused our red-wing to tarry with us. We stand our ground. There was something far more important to this adventure than a doubting thought can see. There are elements of creation that only kindliness, faith and love reveal. What we saw in the friendship of Cheer was the gift of these qualities. As he flew away we felt so convinced that he was departing that we called our good-bys after him.

"Little John will take care of you, Cheer," called Hi-Bub.

Then we learned the source of the roar we had heard. A wall of hard sleet drove fiercely through the trees. We could not see the far shore of the lake through the curtain of white particles that pelted the earth. The ground was immediately covered. The transition was quick and complete. Winter was instantly at hand.

The adventure was not in the least displeasing to us. Quite to the contrary, we loved it. This was the character of our beloved north country. It is a land that demands something of men, women and children. Sternness and severity are inseparable parts of its charm.

We were out in the storm with upturned faces and outspread arms as if to embrace this spirit of the north. "Thith ith thwell, Tham Cammel, thith ith thwell!" cried Hi-Bub, eyes closed as he faced the wind, cheeks glowing red from the touch of cold and pelting of sleet.

The temperature continued to drop, and the sleet changed to fitful spurts of snow. During a slight lull in the storm we crossed from the island to the mainland where our car awaited us. As we passed through the village we left Hi-Bub with his parents. A hurried and not too tearful good-by was said. Then we drove on to our winter's work. Fifty miles to the south we found cold rain stead of snow. A hundred miles—and we had left the storm behind. One hundred and fifty miles of driving brought us to the first sizable city. The clank and clatter, the hurry and excitement of it was a shock to us. It was not easy to become adjusted to an atmosphere so different from that which we had just left. But it helped greatly to know that in the direction of the North Star, which we could see dimly in spite of street lights, the wilderness lived on. It was good to know that Hi-Bub was there—yes, and Little John Deer Foot too.

VI

A DOG NAMED HOBO

I AM deeply grateful that it has been my lot to meet many
people in a way that is both general and personal. Whenever I think of the thousands of upturned faces I have
looked on from the lecture platform, I want to borrow a
much-used word from Hi-Bub's vocabulary and say:
"These are *thwell* people, just *thwell!*"

I am not blind to the evils and problems which seem
to beset human experience. Yet the conviction is growing
with me that our troubles are not such ponderous and difficult things as we have supposed. The enemies to our
happiness are more in the nature of mistakes, errors, su-
perstitions, fears—things that have no power or substance
except that which we give them in ignorance.

See how quickly our notion of nature is changed as the
truth is learned. When we have seen but little of forest
and jungle we fancy it is a constant battlefield. We con-
jure up tales of savagery and bestial ferocity. Yet as we
become acquainted with the world of plant and animal we
find there is a certain charm and peace to it, even in its
severe aspects. We find too a capacity for friendship, devotion and loyalty.

So it is with the human race. Those who love people
little have seen little of them. What is right with our fel-

lows far outweighs what is wrong. I am sure we should hear more of this view. We know that we cannot scold and whip a child into being his best. We cannot abuse ourselves into improvement. Far better a recognition of what is good and commendable than a continuous reprimand for our mistakes.

The storms of the ocean take place on a very thin surface. In the depths there reign calmness and peace. So with the troubles of human experience. The wars and other evils take place on the surface, in the thin scum of selfishness, fear, greed and misunderstanding. In the depth of our true being—in love and Godliness and kindliness— there resides an undisturbed harmony to which we may easily turn.

One of our greatest illusions is that we are separate and different from one another. I have looked down on audiences in cities of the North, South, East and West. Among them have been every nationality and every creed. Yet, when they thought in the common language of nature, let their thoughts dwell in the realm of created and growing things, the same sweet and lovable expression has come to them all.

Yes, people are *"thwell!"* Think of a created being who is mentally capable of brotherly love, honesty, service, goodness, loyalty, happiness. Such is man. Even if he hasn't used these qualities as much as he should, he is capable of them. Small wonder Scripture says of him that "he is fearfully and wonderfully made."

Giny and I talked often along these lines as we went about on our lecture tour. Everywhere we saw the same goodness we loved in Hi-Bub, in Cheer, in Stubby and the rest. In fact, sometimes we saw it revealed in ways and places that were complete surprises.

One evening I sat on the platform of a large auditorium waiting to begin my lecture. Some late-comers entered at the back of the hall. As they walked down the aisle I saw much excitement among those near them, and heard delighted laughter. I looked toward them and rubbed my eyes, unable to believe what I saw. But there was no mistake about it. Down the aisle came a beautiful raccoon, tugging impatiently at the leash which held him. It was a gray raccoon that looked very much like Racket. The creature was being led by a smiling girl of high-school age, who obviously knew the effect this would have on me. The audience waited understandingly for many minutes while Giny and I fondled "Sambo," as he had been named in honor of me. His young mistress had saved him from dogs the previous summer, we learned, and had made a pet of him. "I thought Mrs. Campbell and you might be lonesome for some of your animals at the Sanctuary," she said, "so I brought Sambo over."

Little did she know how much it meant to us to take that lovely creature in our arms. He was accustomed to good treatment by human hands, and he nestled close to us, running his front feet in characteristic manner over our eyes, nose and ears and into our hair. Sambo was one who enjoyed the lecture that night, or at least he enjoyed being at the lecture. He went sound asleep in the girl's arms, and I could hear him snoring softly during some of the most solemn parts of my oration.

At a grammar school I was invited into the third-grade room where I was told a surprise awaited me. I went in to find that a pet crow had taken over the management of things, and thirty children had completely abandoned the pursuit of readin', writin' and 'rithmetic to watch this funny old bird tip over inkwells, steal chalk, pencils and pens, and perch on the head of the eight-year-old boy who owned him. As I walked up to him, Black Beauty, as he had been named, flew to my hand. There he sat talking in a strange tongue, apparently striving to tell me how he happened to be there and how silly it was for all these children to be cooped up in such a cage. Black Beauty was a dandy. He reached in my pocket, plucked out a gold pencil, and dropped it on the floor while the children screamed with delight. The teacher had long since abandoned any hope of order until something was done with Black Beauty. I found a piece of candy in my pocket and offered it to the crow. He wasn't hungry at the time, so he flew across the room carrying the candy in his beak and buried it in a flower pot—bringing another merry outburst from the children.

Back he came and perched on my shoulder. While he screamed in one ear trying to tell me his version of things, the teacher told me hers. It seemed that Gerald, the eight-year-old who owned the crow, had recently moved in from the country. Black Beauty had been a pet at his country home a few miles away. While it nearly broke Gerald's heart, the crow was left behind, for certainly the city was no place to take such a creature. Gerald's family had been living in their new apartment home less than a week when one morning at dawn they heard a sound at the window. There, peering in at them, was Black Beauty. How he found them is one of those mysteries which challenge human explanation. It was a miracle of instinct. However he did it, Black Beauty was with his family again and everyone was happy, particularly Gerald. That day they played together again. Gerald had a little bicycle, and he went dashing up and down the sidewalk with Black Beauty fluttering along trying desperately to ride on the boy's head.

Troubles were not over, however. Schooltime came, and Gerald must take his place in the class. Black Beauty was kept confined the first morning of school and was not released until Gerald was in the school room. About an hour later the teacher of the third grade and all the students were startled by a great commotion at one of the windows. There was Black Beauty, who had performed another miracle of instinct and perseverance and located his young master again. The teacher asked the students to be quiet, and vainly hoped the bird would go away. But who can keep quiet when a crow is pecking at the window pane, fluttering and trying to force his way in, screaming raucously all the while? In desperation, the teacher opened the window and admitted the determined crow. Immediately the bird flew over and perched on Gerald's head, to the delight of all the children.

No book "larnin'" was accomplished that day in the third grade, though surely something very valuable about kindness and faithfulness was learned from Gerald's pet. Black Beauty had the time of his life. He was the center of attention and loved it. He went about the room getting acquainted with everyone present. Whenever a child's hand was held out to him he hopped up on it. He called and talked and scolded. This scene was repeated the second day and the third day, which was the time I witnessed it. I heard later that it was necessary to keep Black Beauty in a cage until after school hours all that winter, so that Gerald and the other children might gain an education.

On the outskirts of an Indiana town I was invited to call at a country home to see a woodchuck that was hibernating in a barrel, which stood in an unheated shed. It had been a pet for several years, and each winter this same barrel had been prepared for its winter sleep. I found the little creature deeply buried in rolls of cotton and cloth. Its breathing was slow and measured. As I looked at it I got a good idea of how our woodchucks now in their underground homes would be carrying on their long sleep. I could handle this somnolent creature without disturbing its dreams in the least. It had a most peaceful expression, as if hibernating were one of the greatest experiences in life. Let the world have a winter if it wished. The little old woodchuck would slumber on, perhaps dreaming of infinite gardens of carrots, celery, turnip tops, beets, cantaloupes, and everything else that grows. This groundhog had been asleep two months when I saw it, and it still had at least three months of this supersnooze to go. His sides were rolling in fat, and there was no doubt that he had the reserve energy to carry out his program.

Once during an assembly of a junior high school I asked

how many of the students had pet animals at home. Two-thirds of the six hundred boys and girls present raised their hands. A few more questions from me brought out some amazing facts. One boy had a collection of twenty snakes in his basement. It was a source of hysteria for his mother and an annoyance to his father—but the snakes stayed on because when any idea of disposing of them was expressed the boy broke out in tears.

Another basement was equally monopolized by an accumulation of turtles, toads and frogs. Each one of the odd creatures had a name and each one was precious to the little girl who was their keeper.

Still another home had a guinea-pig problem. Two pairs had been purchased to begin with. These pairs had young ones, and those young ones had young, and so on and on. They kept multiplying and multiplying, but the boy who owned them didn't want to dispose of any of them. Where that story ended I do not know.

Dogs were the most popular pets, but there were many youngsters who had cats, birds, horses or ponies. One boy had a pet red fox, another an opossum and still another a four-foot alligator!

Is there kindness in the world, you ask? Yes, there is. Every pet story I heard that day was a biography of kindness and love. Look down under the surface of this life and you will find how good is the world and how naturally fine are the people in it.

About this time there was a note from Hi-Bub. He would never take any prizes for his penmanship. His lines ran hither and yon as if they were following a chipmunk.

Between us, however, Giny and I managed to decipher it. Everything was going pretty well with him. He did get zero in arithmetic one day. It was Old Charley's fault, he said. There was no mention of Little John Deer Foot. We were disappointed for we didn't want to lose the Indian boy. Possibly it wasn't exactly right to mention such 'maginaries in writing, we figured. Besides, there was a very exciting bit of news which probably was the most important thing in Hi-Bub's thoughts at the moment. He had a dog! That was in addition to the three cats and one rabbit he had already brought in. "Mom says she is afraid to see me coming home from school because she doesn't know what I'll bring next," the letter said. The dog's name was Hobo. No one knew where he came from. He just appeared one day running down the railroad tracks. "I guess he isn't very pretty," wrote Hi-Bub. "Mom says he isn't. His tail curls and Daddy says it's so the fleas can loop the loop." It wasn't hard for us to picture Hobo as the sort of a saucy little mongrel just designed for Hi-Bub. "Mom asks me please don't bring anything else home," his letter concluded. Then after his shaky signature we read: "P.S. I hope I don't."

VII

A LECTURE FOR TONY

IT WAS early December when our lecture schedule brought us back to a Wisconsin city. I had been looking forward particularly to my lecture in this town. There was a certain sentiment attached to the place, for here we had first met Hi-Bub. He was just beginning his education then, and I gave a program at his grade school. I remember how his beaming face stood out amid all the hundreds who thronged the assembly hall. There is a reason for such experiences. Our friendships in the world are not accidental. Emerson, who lived so close to the heart and purpose of things, tells us it is "not for nothing one face, one character, one fact, makes much impression on [us], another none." Our lives had need of Hi-Bub's friendship, and I like to believe he had need of ours. Now this city was more important to us because in it this blessing had begun.

My lecture was to be given in the auditorium of a large church not far from Hi-Bub's former school. We arrived early to see that the motion-picture equipment was properly prepared. Among the first to enter the auditorium were some people who knew and loved the northwoods. Giny and I were soon in earnest conversation with them.

We talked enthusiastically about certain lakes, streams and wooded areas we all knew.

In the midst of this conversation I heard, or thought I did, a thin voice say, "Hello, Tham Cammel." Couldn't be, of course, so I kept on talking.

"Hello, Tham Cammel," came the words again in such a strong tone that there was no doubt of their reality.

I turned around and there stood Hi-Bub in person! Beside him was his daddy, and both of them looked at us as if they expected us to faint with surprise. I wasn't far from doing that very thing. For a moment I couldn't say a word. I shook my head and rubbed my eyes in bewilderment, while Hi-Bub let little giggles slip past the hand that partially covered his mouth.

"Hi-Bub, Hi-Bub!" I finally burst out. "You old lumberjack! You timber cruiser! You woodsman! You pioneer! You are the biggest surprise I ever saw. How did this happen?"

"Happen?" put in his daddy, casting a wise look at his boy. "Whenever that fellow wants anything, it always happens. He's been planning this for a long time. A friend of his here wrote him you were coming. So I had to drive over two hundred miles to bring him to your lecture!"

By this time Giny had her arms about the happy Hi-Bub. We were discourteous to our other friends, I fear, though I am sure they understood. Hi-Bub was the center of things for the moment. We plied him with questions.

The lecture was late starting that night because our

conversation was not finished in time. We sat at one side of the auditorium hearing about Hobo, the new dog, the cats, the rabbit, school and many other important things. Hobo was a "thwell dog," we were informed. He didn't like to take a bath, but he took one when he had to and then immediately hunted up some dirt to roll in. He followed Hi-Bub to school almost every day and waited outside until school was over.

"But how about Little John Deer Foot?" I asked.

Hi-Bub shot a glance at me to see if I was making sport of him and his 'maginary friend. Apparently my expression was satisfying, for in soft, sincere tones he told me of the doings of the Indian boy. Little John Deer Foot was having trouble with Old Charley the bear. Old Charley didn't want to go to bed. Like many children he was using every excuse he could to stay up, Hi-Bub revealed seriously. Every day it was the same thing. Little John would say to him, "Charley, you mutht go to thleep." Then Old Charley would say, "I'm thirthty. I'll go to the creek and get a drink, then I'll go to thleep." Old Charley would be gone so long the Indian boy would have to go after him. Maybe he would find the bear miles away, trying to get in a cabin. On the side, Hi-Bub's daddy told me that very thing was happening. Old Charley was not in hibernation as yet, and almost every day some new kind of bear capers were reported, all of which were charged to him.

During the lecture Hi-Bub and his daddy sat in the front row. I could hear the boy laughing at the scenes and making his own comments. In the midst of the lecture the film broke. "I 'thpect Old Charley did that," I heard him say.

Afterward Hi-Bub stood right beside me until the usual conversation and comments were over. I could see there was something special on his mind. Presently it came out.

"Tham Cammel," he said.

"Yes, Hi-Bub," said I, bending down to his level.

"Well—Tony couldn't come."

"Tony couldn't come? Who in the world is Tony?"

"That is the little friend who wrote you were to be here," explained Hi-Bub's daddy. "The youngster is in a bad way. He is in bed and may have to remain there for a long time. It happened suddenly. Pretty tough on him. What hurts him worst of all is that he can't see your pictures."

"Tony feelth awful, Tham Cammel," added Hi-Bub, a distressed look in his eyes where joy was so natural. "He duthn't laugh any more."

"He is a sad little tyke," said the daddy. "We saw him for a while today."

"Yeth." Hi-Bub picked up the lead again. "An' hith mom theth he mutht laugh and be happy if he want-th to be well. But he duthn't. He jutht lie-th th-till and lookth thad."

"That's too bad," I said sympathetically. "Couldn't you make him happy, Hi-Bub? You are so happy yourself."

"No," said the boy, quite dejectedly. "I tried to be funny but I gueth I didn't do very well. He theth he duthn't feel like being happy. He wanted . . ."

Hi-Bub hesitated and looked at me with that appeal

that, as his father says, always gets him what he wants.

"I with he could have come tonight," he added.

There was an idea developing in my thought. "Hi-Bub," I said. "I wonder if we can't do something for Tony to help him be happy."

"What?" asked the boy, looking up expectantly.

"Well—you say he wanted to see my pictures. Now I have tomorrow morning free. If you think Tony would like it, suppose we take our pictures over and show them to him right in his own room. We could arrange it so he would just sit up in bed to see them. What do you think of that plan?"

There was no question about what Hi-Bub thought of it. With a "Whe-e-e-e" he ran over and threw his arms around me, his eyes again flashing happiness.

"Oh boy, oh boy—that will be thwell!" he cried. "Tony ith gonna be happy—he'th gonna laugh, I betcha."

"Yes, Hi-Bub," I said. "But first you must find out if it is the right thing to do. You must ask his mother if she wants us, and if she does, what would be the best time."

"Oh, yeth—she want-th uth!" affirmed Hi-Bub. "Th-he thed about ten o'clock."

"Now wait a minute," I said, wrinkling my forehead. "You mean that you had already planned this and made the arrangements?"

"Yeth," exclaimed Hi-Bub. "I told Tony you would come. Oh boy, oh boy!" He went dancing away in high glee.

I looked up understandingly at his daddy.

"You see what I mean?" he asked. "When that fellow
sets his mind on something, he gets it."

At promptly ten o'clock the next morning we were at
Tony's house. His mother was expecting us all right, just
as Hi-Bub had said. "You are kind to come," she commented as she admitted us. "Hi-Bub asked if it would be
all right if you did. There couldn't be anything better
for Tony. He has been discouraged, and felt so bad when
he couldn't go to your program."

"Tony is going to be the smallest audience I ever had,"
I said, "and maybe the greatest."

Tony proved to be a sad-looking little fellow. He shook
hands with me without comment, though there was a look
of interest in his eyes. "Tony is tired of his bed," said his
mother, as she braced him up on pillows. "He's going to
get well and play again the way he used to with Hi-Bub.
But he must be very quiet for a while, and he must be—he
simply must be happy and cheerful." She flashed a mean-
ingful glance at the youngster, but Tony certainly didn't
look very happy.

We set up our equipment, darkened the room and began
to show the pictures. The audience consisted of Tony, his
mother, Hi-Bub and his daddy, Giny and me. It wasn't
long before I learned that I was simply the operator of
the machine. Hi-Bub was the narrator. It was his show
and should be, for he knew what had to be done.

"That'th Th-tubby the chipmunk, Tony," he cried,
pointing a stiff little finger. "Look at 'im, look at 'im."

Tony did look at 'im. His comment was "My!"

"There come-th Patty," exclaimed Hi-Bub, "Look at 'im. Look at 'im."

"What's Patty?" asked Tony, the first full words he had said.

"He'th a woodchuck, dumbbell," said Hi-Bub. "Oh boy, he'th funny. Look at 'im eat a carrot."

"My!" said Tony with increasing interest.

"Hey, lookut, lookut!" shouted the excited Hi-Bub, grabbing Tony by the ear and jerking his head. "That'th Noothanth the red thquirrel. Watch him run out on that rope. Lookut, he'th gonna fall off."

Nuisance the red squirrel did fall off, a tiny tumble that hurt him not one bit, and yet accomplished a miracle. Tony laughed—a real, spontaneous, giggly laugh.

"An', Tony, Tony!" ranted the irrepressible Hi-Bub. "Here come-th Cheer. Oh boy, he'th a thwell bird. Lookut hith wingth. Lookut him th-trut."

By this time Tony wasn't missing a thing. He was leaning forward, not even using the support of his pillows. His own thin little hand was raised again and again as he pointed to things in the pictures. Repeatedly he laughed outright.

For our part, we were watching the pictures but little. The two children before us were our principal interest, though we stole side glances at Tony's mother to see her wiping away sly tears as Tony rose to the occasion. Hi-Bub's daddy spent his time looking at his son with unrestrained pride.

Hi-Bub had all admiration coming. I know that I

never have and never will sway an audience as he did that day. Tony was completely carried away. He forgot himself, forgot his confinement, forgot his discomfort and gave himself up to natural joy. He was calling all the animals by name and watching excitedly for each new stunt they did.

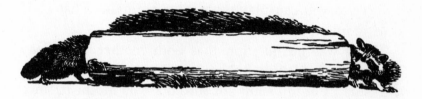

When the film was finished and the last scene had flickered off the screen, Tony was laughing as loudly as Hi-Bub. He even found the energy to engage in a brief boxing match with his former playmate. We had to interrupt this, however, for Hi-Bub's enthusiasm knew no bounds. He imagined that now that the laugh had come to Tony, there was nothing left to do but dress him and start him in a football game.

"That was wonderful medicine for him," said his mother. "You have no idea how we've tried to awaken his spirit. It seemed he didn't want to get well. Now— well, if this will only last!"

"I have another idea," I said. "Tony, did you like the pictures?"

"Oh, my—yes!" said Tony, in a way that left no doubt.

"Did you like the animals?"

"Oh, my!"

"And did you like the woods?"

Tony just looked his affirmative answer.

"Well, then," I continued, "here is my idea. If you will keep happy and help yourself get well—if you will try to be like Cheer, the red-winged blackbird, and give out joy to everyone around you—then when you are strong enough, Giny and I will invite you to come up and stay with us so you can play with those animals. That is, if your mother approves."

There was no question that both mother and Tony highly approved. "Hi-Bub told us of your generous offer," she said. "I didn't know for sure that you meant it, since we were strangers to you. But I am sure it gives Tony a reason to be happy and to get well."

I looked at Hi-Bub. "You mean that Hi-Bub had already told you we wanted Tony?" I asked.

"Why, yes, he did—yesterday."

"Splendid!" I said, trying to save the situation. "Thank you, Hi-Bub."

I glanced over at his daddy. "You see what I mean?" said he.

We stood beside our cars saying good-by. Hi-Bub and his daddy would be driving north to their home. We were going south.

"Tham Cammel," said Hi-Bub, who was trying to drag out the farewell as long as possible.

"Yes, Hi-Bub."

"Would you be comin' home at Chrithmuth?"

"Oh, it would be fun to do that, Hi-Bub," I exclaimed.

"but I am afraid we can't. You see, we wouldn't have any place to stay."

"Couldn't you th-tay at the Thanctuary?" asked Hi-Bub. He had practiced a long time to say that last word.

"No, our cabin isn't built for winter. We would be very cold there."

"Couldn't you th-tay with uth?" he persisted.

I laughed. "You know your cabin is already filled with your family. I am afraid we would have to sleep with Hobo."

"He'th a thwell dog," commented Hi-Bub.

"Yes—but I think he wouldn't want us to crowd him. No, Hi-Bub, I guess Giny and I can't get up there for Christmas, though we would like to, if our cabin were the right kind."

We said our good-bys, promising to see one another in the spring. But there was a funny little look in Hi-Bub's eyes that Giny and I both noticed.

VIII

DESIGN FOR CHRISTMAS—À LA HI-BUB

ABOUT a week later Giny and I received a very welcome letter. The postmark was our own home town, the handwriting that of a friend.

What a wealth of heavenly good is wrapped up in that one word *friend*. It gets interwoven one way or another with everything that is right and desirable in life.

It is rather hard to define, though. I discovered that one day early in our experience with Hi-Bub. He had come to the island for one of his visits that were then just assuming some degree of regularity.

"Well, well—here is our little friend," I exclaimed by way of welcome, then partly to myself I added, "There is no more beautiful adventure in life than just the coming of a real, enduring friend."

The statements did not escape Hi-Bub. He was busy about the woods for a while greeting the creatures who had now learned that his coming was the signal that a feast would begin. Presently he was back at my side.

"Tham Cammel," he said, in the tone and manner which always began a discussion of some sort.

"Yes."

"Wh-wh-what ith a friend?" If he was one of them, he wanted to know why and what made him that way.

I was taken aback for a moment. Questions about chipmunks, skunks, red-backed mice, flowers, trees and such things were expected and I had most answers ready. In response to the queries of Hi-Bub I had delivered long dissertations on both the real and fanciful things of the world, but I had never before been asked anything so challenging as to define a friend. In fact, I guess I had thought you didn't define one. You can be a friend, or have one—but to get it into a formula hadn't occurred to me.

"Well, Hi-Bub," I said stalling for time and thought, "I guess we can say it this way: a friend is someone you love a lot."

He looked up very seriously, his little forehead wrinkled and his eyes half closed.

"But—ithn't that everyone?" he asked.

Now there is one that will stop you. His new question was a revelation of his unspoiled view of life. With him the vision was still clear that creation is naturally good and lovable. He lived at that point in Scripture that declares, "God created man in His own image ... and God saw every thing that He had made, and, behold, it was very good." He had not learned that people sometimes take on themselves unnatural traits, and become dishonest, selfish and unfriendly. He had not learned that this race of man created in God's image had in error separated itself into races, nationalities, creeds and colors. If a friend was someone you love a lot, then everyone was a friend, for he had no notion that there could be anyone he didn't love.

"Yes, that is right, Hi-Bub," I said. I searched for

some way to pursue the definition without destroying his admirable attitude. "Friendliness is found everywhere when one keeps his heart right as you do. But friends as we usually think of them are just a little different. Friends are people who are close to us."

I hadn't said anything convincing or important yet, and by the puzzled look on the lad's face I knew it. Trying to shift the burden of explanation I suggested we look in the dictionary. It didn't help much, for its words were too cold. It just said, "One attached to another by esteem, respect, affection." Hi-Bub didn't care about that. While I read it, he fingered through an animal picture book and didn't have to hear a word I said. I tried some poetic lines from a book of quotations, but he still looked at animal pictures.

"Come on out in the woods, Hi-Bub," I said, rising and leading the way. "I believe we can understand this friendship business there."

He always wanted to go into the woods, so out we went. We followed the trail that circles the island, Hi-Bub carefully picking his steps so he made little noise. Indians walked that way, he had been told, and he would too.

"Now, see those hills in the distance?" I asked when we had reached the right point.

He did.

"What do you suppose we would find up there among the trees?"

Well, he was sure there were deer there. There would be chipmunks, porcupines, squirrels, rabbits, woodchucks and birds too.

6—OWOC

"Do you love them all, Hi-Bub?"

"Yeth."

"Even though you never saw those particular animals, you love them anyway?"

"Yeth," he said with a little emphasis born of impatience.

"That is right, you love them just the same as you love Stubby, or Nuisance, or Patty. You love them all. But these animals on the island, you can play with—they come up to you and you like to have them around. The animals on our island, then, are just the same as the others, only they are not afraid of you. They come to you for food and they make you laugh and be happy. Friends do things for one another. So these island animals are your friends. Do you see?"

Hi-Bub nodded his head, at the same time tugging at my hand. Illustrated with the ever-interesting parable of animals, the definition of a friend was becoming clear to him. Besides, the mere mention of his island pals excited him. "Let-th go and find a friend," he said with a laugh.

Our quest was not so easy. It was midday and the animals had hidden from the strong sun. We looked for Stubby, but he was nowhere around. We looked for Nuisance, but he was missing. We called and coaxed, but for a long time not a living thing responded. Then suddenly out of a hole almost at our feet popped Patty the woodchuck. His coming was so quick and unexpected it startled us.

"There you are, Hi-Bub," I exclaimed as he held out a

peanut to reward the creature for his devotion. "Now do you understand what a friend is?"

"Yeth, I know," said the delighted youngster. "It ith thomeone who popth up when you need 'im."

Not a bad definition of a friend at that—just someone who pops up when you need him.

The letter we received came from friends who fit that definition perfectly. Through many years of acquaintance they have always "popped up" when there was a service to perform. Their cozy forest home lies but a few miles from our Sanctuary. Their letter bore three signatures: Ray, Ada and June. Ray was a forest ranger, strong, capable, fearless, knowing the woods as few men do. Ada was the wife and mother, in love with family, home and the wildwood in which they lived. June was their dark-eyed, dark-haired daughter slightly older than our Hi-Bub, who had such beauty of feature and character that she was the center of attention wherever she went. These fine people had been our companions on many wilderness adventures.

Their letter reflected considerable excitement. It disposed of the greeting, and then got down to its purpose. "A little bird has been telling us a secret," the letter ran. "It is a nice little bird, and we won't tell you what kind it is. The secret is that your schedule is such you could come to the northwoods for Christmas. The same bird says that you would come if you had a place to stay. We told the bird you do have a place to stay. Our home is just yearning for you, and so are our hearts. We have a guest room, and we have plans for the happiest Christmas we ever knew. Will you come, and make these plans come true?"

"Blessed Ray and Ada," I said as Giny finished reading the letter aloud. "They would be the ones to suggest that."

"We can do it, can't we?" asked Giny anxiously.

"Well, I had planned to do some writing at that time," I said cautiously.

"But if we go up there, you'll have more to write about," she declared.

Our letter went back on the first mail. We would be glad to come, we said. We could arrive the day before Christmas and stay for several days. We requested an old-fashioned Christmas. "Just one question we want to ask," our letter said. "That little bird that has been whispering so much—by any chance did it lisp somewhat, and pronounce my name Tham Cammel?"

"It will be an old-fashioned Christmas," read the reply that came immediately. "There will be turkey, a Christmas tree, a grab bag—fun, food and friends. We will meet you at the train." A postscript added, "Yes, the little bird did lisp, and he called you Tham Cammel. If you see him, don't you dare scold him. He did this in a way that was all too cute. Besides, if you had just written us as you should that you wanted to come, the little bird could have saved his whispering. Incidentally, we believe this same whispering, lisping bird is quite smitten with our June!"

IX

CHRISTMAS WRAPPINGS

WHEN Alice slipped through the mirror into the looking-glass world, she found hardly more miraculous changes than we did when we arrived in the north country the day before Christmas. The morning crackled with cold as our three-car train—a baggage car, a day coach and one Pullman sleeper—huffed and puffed into the station. The sun was peering over the eastern horizon, looking weak and inadequate to heat up such a frosty world.

While we slept the world had undergone metamorphosis. From our Pullman window the night before we had looked at the clustered houses and blinking lights of the city. Through the same window at dawn we saw the silent forests of cedars, balsams and pines silhouetted against the morning glow. Everywhere lay the glistening white carpet of snow spread by nature to protect her solitude, softening even the tread of the winds.

The train came to a squeaky and jerky stop. Our porter helped us to the platform, then deserted us as quickly as he could within the bounds of courtesy. "It sure is cold!" he said, his hand shaking so he could hardly accept the remembrance I offered him.

"A merry Christmas to you!" I said. His teeth chattered so much that his response sounded very little like "same to you," though I am sure that is what he tried to say. He was constituted for other climes. As soon as he could, he shut the Pullman door, waved through the window a good-by accompanied by a sort of "you-poor-things" expression, and hastened to sit on a steam pipe.

Giny and I looked about us with joy. The little town was all huddled up, packed in cotton for the winter. Windows were thick with frost. Graceful plumes of vaporous smoke reached upward from the chimneys. Streets were paved with hardened snow and the borders of sidewalks were lined with high drifts formed by snow shovels.

Our train was late and so were the friends who were to meet us. Being late makes no difference in this country, however. There is plenty to do but the tasks can be done at one time as well as another.

We took our bags and walked toward the station. The snow creaked musically under our feet. No other passengers had left the train. The light clean air delighted our lungs and frost took playful nips at our noses and cheeks.

Up forward there was much activity. Our engine was enveloped in a cloud of steam. The engineer in the cab looked at his watch and then glared critically at the men who were unloading a consignment of express from the baggage car.

"What are you lookin' at that thing for?" the station agent called to him. "You're never on time nohow."

"Wanted to see how many hours it takes you to do five minutes' work" came the answer.

"Ever read your timetable?" the other pursued his

point. "It'd surprise you. You were supposed to be here fifty-five minutes ago. What do you do—go huntin' every morning?"

"I was on time once," drawled the engineer. "Wasn't nobody round. I had to sit here till you got up, dressed and had your breakfast before you'd come down and get the mail. I might as well play along and watch the scenery. It's better to look at than your homely face. How cold is it?"

"Twenty below—according to my nose."

"Can't go by that thing. It's always sticking in somebody's business. What does the thermometer say?"

"Fifteen below, but it's busted, I think. Ever since the time it touched fifty-four below it won't work right."

"Fifty-four below! By your nose?"

"Didn't have any nose that day—it was just an icicle," said the agent, sniffing in memory of the record cold wave.

"Well, too bad you didn't winterkill," said the engineer unsympathetically. "Where's Lem these days?"

"He's loggin'—over in Forest County."

"Where's big Steve?"

"Loggin'—up in Michigan."

"Where is your boy?"

"Road buildin' up in Alaska."

The engineer rubbed the cold from his cheeks. "Seems like everyone works round here 'cept you," he commented. "Come on, get the frost out of your joints and unload them sacks. You can't be as dead as you act."

"What do you care?" was the saucy answer. "You're goin' no place and you got all day to do it."

The bantering went on. Giny and I walked away stamping our feet and clapping our hands to encourage circulation. The cold was creeping through our garments. We rubbed our cheeks and noses too. While this is a dry cold and therefore not raw or chilling, it is quick-freezing.

Now came a car squeaking on the crusted snow, honking, radiator steaming. The windows were almost completely covered with thick frost. Two small circles on the windshield had been scraped clear. Out of these openings peered the laughing eyes of our friends Ray, Ada and June. All were calling a merry welcome.

The car stopped and a door opened. Out came the funniest-looking something or other we had seen in a long time. It was like a large stuffed doll—or perhaps over-stuffed is the better word. It half tumbled from the car and stood for a moment facing us. I guess it was facing us, for it was difficult to determine whether it was coming or going. I never saw more woolen clothes in one small spot before—woolen breeches, woolen coat, woolen mittens and a huge woolen scarf topped by a woolen stocking cap. Presently from somewhere in this mound of clothing came a muffled little voice, "Hello, Tham Cammel and Mithuth Cammel."

"Hi-Bub!" I cried, as Giny and I ran to him. "Are you down in there somewhere? Come on out where we can see you!"

We unwound a yard or two of scarf, to reveal the beaming face of our fine lad. The others alighted from the car now, and there was a general outburst of greetings that made the trainmen cease their work and look our way.

"June, come here," I exclaimed to the girl who was standing near. "How you have grown! You are more beautiful than ever. Let me look at you."

"Yeth! Let me look too!" interposed Hi-Bub, as he thrust his way directly in front of the laughing girl. His eyes sparkled the same way they did when he saw Cheer. "You're a thwell girl," he said with feeling.

June just flashed a smile that sparkled like the snow in the morning sun.

"I'll tell you why we were late," explained Ray and Ada as we gripped their hands. "Hi-Bub was so anxious to come to the train that we stopped for him. They had about three layers of clothes on him and we waited until several more were put on. Then the heater in our car stopped working and the windows frosted over. It has been an exciting morning."

"I wuth gonna bring Hobo," shouted Hi-Bub, trying to talk above the general babble. "Only he didn't want to come. You thee he duthn't know you very well yet."

We vowed we would win the affections of Hobo so he would be on the reception committee on our next trip. The excited conversation continued while we loaded our baggage. Just as we were about to start we paused a moment to hear the finals of the tête-à-tête between the engineer and station agent. The engineer had backed the train slightly to release the brakes. That was all his sparring partner needed.

"Now that's what I been a-tellin' you——" the agent yelled. "You don't know which one of them gadgets to push. You're a-goin' the wrong way. You can't get anywhere doin' that. Why don't you get a wheelbarrow—something you know how to run?"

"Course I only been doin' this thirty-five years," called the other.

"Some folks never learn nothin'!"

"Aw, go back to your hibernatin' with the rest of the skunks," said the engineer, making the wheels of the engine spin. "I'll see you in the morning."

"You'll never get back in one day the way you're a-goin'," taunted the agent, trying to be heard above the noise of escaping steam. "You'll get mixed up and end in Lake Superior. What you need there is an engineer. You can shovel coal all right but——"

The engineer ended the conversation with a couple of toots and a wave of the hand, while the agent turned chuckling to his work.

We closed the car doors and headed for home and breakfast. There was a short stop at Hi-Bub's house. We paused to greet his parents, and of course to meet Hobo.

The latter was just the kind of dog I expected. He was one-hundred-percent pure mongrel, and didn't care. He was a small dog with big ambitions. There was no question but that he planned to run the whole town. His color was hard to describe. I had never seen such a mess on any paint card. One ear stood up; the other folded down to give him a sort of "hat-on-the-side-of-the-head" appearance. There was a black spot over one eye that made him seem always to be winking. His tail was unreasonably long and so curled it almost completed a second loop. Hobo wasn't trained. He didn't know anything about sitting up or shaking hands. But he was a bundle of energy, and reports indicated that he was minding everybody's business except his own from morning until night.

"I hope we will be friends, Hobo," I said, stroking his head.

At that moment he discovered another dog about a block away and left us all without even a bark for good-by.

"Surely we will see you again during our visit, Hi-Bub," said Giny as we were taking our leave.

"You thure will, Mithuth Cammel," said the boy confidently.

"Are there plans afoot?" I asked.

All of them laughed. "Indeed there are plans afoot," said Ada. "Hi-Bub has arranged to have his Christmas at home today. Then tomorrow he is to be with us for our Christmas. Won't that be fun?"

"Marvelous!" I exclaimed. "Hi-Bub, you are a schemer. Two Christmases in one year—what a manager you turned out to be!"

X

ALMOST A CHRISTMAS TREE

AT THE home of our fine hosts, over buckwheat pancakes and farm sausage, we talked of Christmas plans.

"Are we really going to have an old-fashioned Christmas?" I asked.

Yes, we were going to have an old-fashioned Christmas. A turkey almost the size of an ostrich hung on the back porch. There were to be stuffing, cranberry sauce, plum pudding, black walnuts, too many vegetables, presents galore, excitement and exhaustion for everyone.

"What, no sleigh bells?" I teased. Yes, some way or other there would be sleigh bells.

"Marvelous!" I said. "And may Giny and I go into the kitchen and help with the preparations?"

This was a test all right. Not many of the best of friends want you in their kitchens. But even this privilege was not too much to ask of Ada and Ray. Yes, we could go into the kitchen. In fact, they had anticipated that Giny would bake the pies. I could put on a white apron and a chef's cap, and get in everyone's way while I made the dressing, mashed the potatoes, spilled the gravy and sampled everything I could reach.

"And are we going to put the food right on the table in big dishes, and set the turkey out where everyone can watch it carved?" I asked, thinking of the hotel dinners where one never sees the fowl until it comes in thinly sliced, draped like blankets over a small mound of dressing.

Yes, the food would be right on the table, and the carving of the turkey a public spectacle. In fact, plans were that I should do the carving!

"Blessings upon blessings," I declared. "I'm going to sit in that big chair now and indulge in the joy of anticipation."

"Indeed you will not!" interposed Ada. "You and Ray have work to do—important work. Today you must go out into the woods and get our Christmas tree, then put it up and trim it. Giny and I have a big job to do on the turkey. Now have another pancake, and then let's get busy. Christmas is no time to rest, especially if it is to be an old-fashioned Christmas."

Breakfast over, Ray and I mounted our snowshoes and headed out into the forest in quest of a Christmas tree. The atmosphere was light and invigorating, and it put energy into our pace. Little showers of hardened snow flakes flew ahead of our strides, making the soft musical sound known and loved by those who travel in winter's solitude.

We had gone very little distance, however, when we heard a voice calling to us, "Wait a minute, you two— please!" We halted and looked around to see June coming after us, swinging her half-sized snowshoes like a veteran. "Mother said I had better go along," she said as she drew near. "She's afraid you might get lost if you go alone."

"Snowshoeing in the brush is tough, young lady," I said doubtfully. "We would love your charming company, if you can stand the pace."

"Don't worry about her," said Ray, unmistakable pride in his words and laugh. "Likely it will bother you and me to keep up with her."

Laughing and tossing her pretty head, June started out. I realized she needed no sympathy. Her stride was perfect. This little lady had been raised in the forest. She grew up accustomed to its ways and its demands. Her mannerisms reflected the influence of nature. I noted how easy, patient and unhurried were her movements. With wisdom born of much experience she selected the best route through the forest with its many obstacles. She had taken the silence of wilderness into her very character. While the expression in her eyes showed deep happiness and keen appreciation of her surroundings, her words were few. Obviously she loved to be alone. While Ray and I looked about for our Christmas tree, she went far ahead, circling and reappearing to us at most unexpected places.

In prospect the task of getting a Christmas tree in that country seemed easy. The forest was filled with numberless balsam trees and black spruce. We had told Giny and Ada that we would be gone only a few minutes. Our instructions were to bring in a big tree—not too tall, for the ceiling was low—but it must have a wide spread.

We found one such tree within ten minutes' walk from the house. However, it was near the roadside and Ray suggested that it would look beautiful there the year around, so why destroy it for just a few hours of pleasure?

At the edge of a large swamp we found a beautiful spruce of medium height, whose branches spread widely. Ray took the ax in hand and surveyed the tree for a moment.

"Been growing here about twenty years," he commented, stroking a branch admiringly. "I remember when it wasn't knee-high."

June had come up that moment and stood looking at the tree with an expression of regret on her face. "It looks mighty pretty there, doesn't it?" she said.

"Sure does," agreed her father. "Let's take a look for a balsam over on that hillside. Balsam will last longer indoors anyway."

So over to the hillside we went. There were some beautiful balsam trees there. Ray picked out one with thick foliage and advanced toward it with the ax.

"That tree has produced a lot of seeds," I commented, noticing the cone stems on the upper branches. "It's mighty useful in reforesting this area."

"That's right," said Ray, looking about for another prospect. "This was a bad fire area in here, and these balsam trees have helped a lot by growing so fast. Let's see what's on the other side of the hill."

On the other side of the hill were some especially fine trees, and almost any one of them might have met our requirements. But in each case there was some excuse to withhold the ax. One had a bird's nest in it, and it was possible the bird might come back in the spring. Another that grew close to the ground furnished shelter with its

lower branches to a rabbit, and it didn't seem just fair to take that one. Still another showed the scars left by a wild cat as the creature stood sharpening its claws like a domestic cat.

"We wouldn't want to take that," said Ray. "It's nice to come on such things when you are hiking. Anyway, these are needed on this hillside to prevent erosion. Let's go on into that flat country. There must be some good ones there."

There were some good trees in the flat country, but

again we found one excuse after another for not cutting them. So it was with the big swamp which Ray wanted to visit. There were some beautiful spruce on a little island in the center of that lowland.

"But they look downright pretty there," Ray insisted. "I'd hate to take one of those. Anyway, that makes good shelter for the deer in hunting season. I saw an old buck lie down in that thicket and stay there in spite of the fact that hunters were searching all around him. Let's see if we can find a tree nearer home—maybe one that the wind has blown over or something."

During all this time June held to her silence, except for a soft little laugh each time Ray and I found an excuse not to cut a tree. She had made many detours to one side or the other of our route, and probably had traveled twice the distance we had. Yet she showed not the least fatigue.

As we walked away from the big swamp my snowshoe caught in a tiny spruce that was nearly buried in the snow. The impact sent me tumbling, and my shoe pulled up the tree, which was only about twelve inches high. No one seemed concerned in the least about my fall. Both June and Ray looked sympathetically at the uprooted tree.

"That's a cute little fellow," said Ray as he picked it up. He and June tried to fit it into the ground again, but it wouldn't stay. Ray carried it along, when I was organized to travel again, holding it up and admiring its growth. "At least four years old," he declared. "Still we destroy it in about ten seconds. Here—let this be a reminder to watch where you step." He forced the roots into my coat collar.

"Now you have been crowned Chief Spruce-in-the-Neck," laughed June.

I let the tree stay where it was as we snowshoed homeward.

Suddenly, to our surprise, we emerged on the road not far from Ray's house. We had been gone three hours and were returning *without a tree.*

"We're on a spot," said Ray, anticipating the reaction we would meet at home. "What do we do now?"

"Hm-m-m, hm-m-m," said June, with a significant flash of her dark eyes.

Giny and Ada heard us removing our snowshoes outside the kitchen door.

"It certainly took you a long time to get a tree in woods that are made of trees," Ada called. "Bring it in right away. We must get busy with our trimming."

Ray and I walked in with sheepish looks on our faces.

"Bring in the tree!" exclaimed Ada with good-natured impatience.

"We did."

"Where is it?"

"Here!" said Ray, and he brought from behind his back our twelve-inch spruce. "Isn't it a beauty? We accidentally pulled it up when we stumbled on it. It would look grand on the table."

Giny and Ada know us pretty well. They stood regarding us with crooked smiles, hands on hips, and toes patting the floor ominously.

"Aw, we didn't want to cut those trees," Ray began. "Why, it takes about twenty years to grow a tree the size and shape you wanted. Then just one stroke with the ax and all the growth is gone. . . ."

But Giny and Ada had reached for the little spruce. "It's a dandy," said Giny stroking its clustered branches. "It would decorate beautifully."

"All right," said Ada resignedly. "June, please get me a flower pot to put it in."

"Mother," said June quietly as she started away.

"Yes, dear."

"Men are funny, aren't they?"

XI

JINGLE BELL

MY FIRST conscious thought the next morning was of *sleigh bells!* Remember, I wanted them in my old-fashioned Christmas. Well, I heard them tinkling even before my eyes were opened.

Sleigh bells are rare things seldom found outside the land of memories, yet as I gave heed I was sure my ears did not deceive me. There was that sound I had learned to love so much in my boyhood days in the farming country of Illinois. At least, it was something like that old-time tinkle. I began to notice it was a little bit thin, and surely it was startlingly close. In fact, if there was a sleigh driving around, it must be right in our bedroom, and we were about to be run over. Then I heard a smothered laugh. Suspiciously I peeked out of a narrow slit in one eye to see Ray looking through a crack in our door, violently shaking a dog collar that had one small bell on it.

"Merry Christmas! Merry Christmas!" he shouted as he saw that I was awake. "Look what I snatched away from Santa Claus as he went by awhile ago. Come on and have a look at this day—you never saw one to beat it."

"Merry Christmas, Ray!" I called back. "That bell certainly did give me a fine dream while it lasted. Don't let the day get away. Giny and I will be right with you."

It was then that I looked out our window into a veritable fairyland! Ray was right; we had never seen greater beauty. Nature had planned an old-fashioned Christmas too. All through the night a soft, feathery snow had been falling, the flight of the flakes straight and steady, not influenced by even the slightest breeze. Before dawn the clouds had completed their tasks and departed. The sun rose into a clear sky lighting a white, glistening, silent wilderness wonderland. The forest had been fitted with a new regal coat of ermine. Everywhere the gentle snow lay exactly as it had fallen. Stumps, branches, limbs, twigs and pine needles were piled high with it. Low balsam trees were completely covered, until they looked like ghostly figures in weird poses, as if a troop of frivolous forest spirits had been surprised and frozen in a grotesque dance. Tall trees had caught armloads of the treasure and were crowned with turbans of fleecy loveliness. Occasionally a high branch would let go its collection. The sparkling crystals floating earthward looked like filings from the stars.

Christmas, blessed Christmas had come! While the morning was still young, the homey home in which we stayed was a whirl of joyous activity. The fireplace was crackling. Giny was rolling out pumpkin and mince pies wholesale. Ada was dressing up the great turkey like an Indian prince. Ray and I were running errands all over the place.

The tiny twelve-inch Christmas tree was dazzling in its finery, and it was engulfed in a growing mound of pres-

ents. Neighbors from near and far came and went, bringing greetings, good will, and smiles along with home-
baked cookies, jams, jellies and preserves "made of berries
picked right in these very woods!"

One family of callers was of just the right make-up to
promote a good snow fight. I had wanted to dive into the
soft drifts and now I had my chance. In a battle that was
a bit on the rough side, snow was tucked down necks, faces
were washed, loosely packed snowballs thrown. I finished
completely buried in a mound that had looked more beautiful and inviting than it felt.

June heard the wild cries incidental to this conflict and
donned a ski suit in record time to come out and get into
it. Ray had warned me not to underrate this slender miss,
and I soon learned what he meant. While I had thought
to frighten her with a shower of snow, I soon found I was
having my own face washed at her hands, and snow was
being tucked down my neck in considerable quantity.

In the midst of this battle Hi-Bub arrived. Yelling delightedly, "Oh boy, oh boy!" he sailed into the melee. His
daddy, who had brought him, caught the spirit of the
thing too. By the time we had finished we all looked like
snowmen of different sizes and shapes. It took ten minutes of brushing with a stiff broom before we were permitted to enter the house again.

"That wuth a thwell fight!" giggled Hi-Bub, particularly pleased that June had elected to sweep the clinging
snow from him.

I spoke with his daddy before he departed. "It is re-
markably generous of you to lend us Hi-Bub for Christ-

mas," I said to him. "I appreciate it very much. The day
wouldn't have been complete if we couldn't have had him
for a little while."

"His Christmas wouldn't have been complete without
this either," answered his daddy, with an understanding
smile. "I hope he won't be any bother to you."

"If he should seem like a bother that would be our mistake and our fault," I commented. "The little tyke has
become a part of me."

"And you are a part of him," said the father warmly,
showing plainly his approval of this trend in his son's life.
God bless a parent who cultivates such unselfishness. Too
often there is jealousy when the youngster reaches for companionship outside the immediate family circle. This man
knew that love is infinite, and that affection is never com-
petitive. He knew the love Hi-Bub felt for us was not
taken away from his own parents, and that he had not less
of his son but really more of him because of this growing
interest. My grip of the man's hand I am sure told him
I understood and appreciated these things.

Our Christmas day developed rapidly. I never knew
so much in the way of happiness and adventure could happen in a few short hours.

Most of the morning Hi-Bub and all of us were in the
kitchen. There were lots of collisions. Someone was always right in the way of everything that had to be done.
That was an essential part of the fun. No Christmas
should be without excitement and confusion.

I was the official taster and I had a full dinner before
the others had a bite. How was the mincemeat for flavor?

Giny wanted to know. How was the pumpkin? How was the dressing for seasoning? How were the cranberries?

The spirit of Old Charley, the gremlin bear, must have taken a hand when the matter of the cranberries was being settled—permanently. After the tasting I was instructed to put them on the back porch where it was cold. I started to carry out the orders, but I didn't get very far. Hi-Bub was right in the route that led to the porch. His head was just low enough that I couldn't see him over the large bowl of cranberries. There was a terrific tangle. He stepped on one of my feet and I stepped on one of his. He gave a yell and so did I. In the mixup the bowl slipped from my hands and down it went with a crash on the floor. Cranberry juice splashed on everyone and everything. Hi-Bub was a mess. Giny's apron was ruined. Ada's dress was spattered. My boots were dripping. Ray had cranberries in the cuffs of his trousers.

"There's your old-fashioned Christmas for you!" cried Ray, as soon as the laughter had died down enough to permit words.

"Oh, oh—our good cranberries!" Giny moaned.

"Oh boy, oh boy!" said Hi-Bub, in a more sober vein than his usual one. "Thith ith a thwell meth!" Any dismay on his part was quickly dispelled by the fact that June was assigned the task of cleaning him up.

"Now we eat canned cranberries," laughed Ada. "Come on—bring the broom, mop, shovel, rake and hoe —we must get this cleaned up, for time is passing."

The debris was soon cleaned up. The next and most dramatic event of our morning was putting the turkey in the oven. It was all stuffed and sewed. I never saw another such bird. It did suggest an ostrich, though perhaps a rather small one. It was a miracle that it went into the oven. We were in a huddle before the stove as it slid in. Then all of us helped close the oven door. That is really getting your fingers into a Christmas day.

Then came a surprise for Giny, Hi-Bub and me.

"Quickly now, get into your warm clothes," said Ray, clapping his hands in enthusiasm. "Get out the snow-shoes—we are headed for the Sanctuary!"

"Whe-e-e-e-e," cried Hi-Bub.

My heart gave a bound of delight. "But the turkey," I protested, "dare we leave that?"

"Yes, we can," declared Ada confidently. "We have it all figured out. The turkey will be cooking six hours. June has agreed to stay and watch it while we have our hike. In four hours we can get to your cabin and back. Then we'll finish the dinner."

"But June will miss the hike," Giny protested.

"She has the woods all the time," said Ada. "Besides, she just loves to cook, don't you, June?"

June nodded happily.

The matter was settled at once for everyone except Hi-Bub. He looked as if he had got caught somewhere between an immovable object and an irresistible force. What to do? Out at the Sanctuary were his animals and the places in which he had had so much fun. Yet here at the house was June.

"Could I thtay here?" he asked.

"Why, yes, if you wish, Hi-Bub," I answered.

"But couldn't June go?"

"No—she wants to cook the turkey."

"Well—well . . ." He looked from one to another for some sort of help.

June supplied what was needed. "Come, Hi-Bub," she said as though the decision was all made. "Let me help you into your clothes. I want you to see the Sanctuary in winter, and then tell me all about it. You and I will sit by each other at dinner, won't we?"

"Yeth, you bet we will!" agreed Hi-Bub, enthusiastically, heading for his toggery.

Yes, June—men are funny, at any age.

"Hurry, then," exclaimed Ada, "let's not waste any time."

We didn't waste any. In a few minutes we were dressed for the adventure and ready to go. Hi-Bub was the over-stuffed doll again, though not quite so bundled up as he had been at the station the previous morning. The temperature had risen somewhat. His little face was left fully exposed, partly so he could see what was going on, but mostly so we could see his happy expression. A small sled was taken along for his convenience. Such short feet and legs were hardly made for wading through drifts and they were not yet ready for snowshoes.

One thing delayed us slightly. We prepared Christmas packages for our pet animals. There was a bag of nuts for the red squirrels. There were bread crumbs, grain, suet and gravel for the birds. A good-sized package of dog biscuit was included for the raccoons, though we felt sure they would not be awake to eat them. At Giny's insistence another supply of this food was placed in a cloth sack for Old Charley.

"Why, he's asleep—I hope," I commented.

"Yes, but we can hang it where he'll find it in the spring," Giny insisted. "Charley is going to have a Christmas present whether he knows it or not."

We drove as far as the road permitted, then left the car at the roadside and cut through the woods toward our lake. Our snowshoes sank through the newly fallen snow, but underneath there was a crust that held us up. Hi-Bub had a great time with his sleigh ride. Like a slave driver, he urged us on faster and faster. The pace kept us from feeling the cold. Ray and I carried packsacks in which were the gifts for our animals. In less than an hour of hiking our snowshoes were singing over the crusted ice of our lake. At last before us, conspicuous among the leafless trees, stood our cabin!

Giny and I have since tried to put into words the feeling we had as we approached our home. We could not do so. There were tears in our eyes and they could not be charged against the cold.

The cabin looked as if it were just a great drift of snow with windows in it. We shoveled our way to the door, opened it and stepped in. There were exclamations of joy as we saw the many familiar books, chairs, tables, dishes—things intimately associated with so much happiness. The place really was cold, however. In fact, it is always colder in an unused cabin than it is outside. We started the fireplace and the oil stove. It took them a long time to make any impression on the temperature. We melted snow to obtain water and then made some tea.

"This is the grandest Christmas gift I ever received," exclaimed Giny. "Just think of being here, sipping tea in our own cabin."

We heard a little chirp outside. Hi-Bub jumped to his feet excitedly. There was Nuisance, his favorite red squirrel, perched up on a snowshoe that had been left sticking in a drift. The creature was eying us with surprise and curiosity. His short bushy tail was whisking back and forth as he endeavored to understand this situation. Probably he was revising all his conclusions about this human species. He had always thought they migrated when winter approached and didn't return until spring. But here they were, dressed differently from the way he had seen before, to be sure—but they were the same people he had known.

"Noothanth! Noothanth!" cried Hi-Bub. He grasped the package of nuts we had brought along and ran to the door. The enthusiastic approach was too much for Nuisance. Letting out a cry, the red squirrel scampered away over the snow and disappeared under the shed.

We cleared a spot on the ground where the nuts could be spread. A few minutes later Nuisance stood in the midst of them eating his fill. Hi-Bub made a calmer and more successful approach to his friend then. We cleared snow from the bird feeding station too, and there we placed the various tidbits we had brought along. The suet was tied in trees, and I had hardly secured the first piece

when a hairy woodpecker came up and dined. We shoveled snow away so that we could see under the house. Our Christmas present for the raccoons was placed there. Since it would not spoil, we knew they would enjoy it whenever they found it.

The time we could stay at our cabin was limited. We closed and locked the door with the promise that we would be back with the first days of spring. Then we donned our snowshoes and headed for the area in which our old black bear had lived. We crossed a small hill and went down into the valley where he had been liberated, and where we had fed him during the previous autumn. The snow showed not a single track. We went a little farther until we could see, reaching out of the snow, the roots of the overturned pine tree where once I had seen Charley assembling leaves and cedar bark. At first sight there was no hint of anything unusual. Everywhere was the blanket of undisturbed snow. Then suddenly Ray grasped my arm. Pointing excitedly toward the roots, he said, "Look—isn't that a little vapor rising?" We moved cautiously toward the place. It was true. There was a plume of vapor rising from among the roots.

"That's Charley," we said in unison. Hi-Bub was so excited we had to restrain him from going there and digging down to the hibernating creature.

Yes, in all probability that was the old black rascal himself. It could have been another bear, but inasmuch as he had prepared this place for himself, in all likelihood our neighborhood nuisance was down under that warming blanket of snow, and this was his breath drifting up through a small chimney it had created. We were careful not to disturb him. Probably it would have been difficult on such a cold day to bring a bear out of sleep, though it is possible to awaken them. Like us, however, they are not in the best of humor when this happens.

"Tham Cammel," said Hi-Bub softly, looking up from his position on the sled.

"Yes, Hi-Bub."

He motioned me to come closer. Obviously what he

had to say was of confidential nature. I knelt beside him.

"I forgot to tell you," he said quietly, his eyes looking down. "Little John put Old Charley to bed. He covered him with—with—you know what. . . ."

"Cedar bark and leaves?" I volunteered.

"Yeth, and then thnow," he went on. "Little John come-th every day to thee him." Hi-Bub shot a look at me to see if my attitude was right.

"I am so glad, Hi-Bub," I said understandingly. "Old Charley needs someone to watch over him. You and I can't do it, of course, but Little John Deer Foot can."

"Yeth!" agreed Hi-Bub, now encouraged. "He told me Old Charley dreamth about bee-th and honey an' he kinda laughth in hith thleep."

"Good!" I exclaimed, so loud that the other members of the party looked around. "Hi-Bub, I wonder why we don't see Little John's tracks around here." I was testing his imagination and he was equal to it.

"Why," he said, looking at me in surprise that I didn't know, "Little John ith an Indian. He knowth how to walk on thnow and not make any trackth."

Oh, wonderful Little John Deer Foot! It seemed there was nothing he couldn't do.

We tied Charley's Christmas present on the limb of a near-by tree. Some bacon rind had been put in to attract his attention. By standing on his hind legs he could reach the bag, tear it open and get the food. Whether or not he would find it, or want it, we would never know—but we had the pleasure of leaving it for the old fellow anyway.

It was mid-afternoon as we started back for the car. In a balsam thicket we flushed a magnificent buck, with a beautiful pair of antlers. He was as surprised to see us as we were to see him. We had supposed all deer were in the great swamps by this time, yarded for the winter. Probably he had supposed all people were yarded up in towns and cities. When we came on him, he did not move at first but just stared at us in blank amazement. His ears went forward, his eyes widened and he held his antlers high. For a moment we wondered if something were wrong with him so that he could not run. He quickly laid our doubts to rest when he rose to his feet and went away into the forest in a series of magnificent leaps that made us gasp in admiration.

We emerged from the woods near the car. Our fingers and toes were numb with cold as we removed our snowshoes, but otherwise we were quite comfortable. The car heater had been put in order, and it wasn't long before our frosted extremities were tingling with warmth.

"I'm so hungry I could take a bite out of this steering wheel," declared Ray with a groan.

We all emphasized our hunger. Hi-Bub went farther than that. "Oh boy, I could eat thith theat!" he exclaimed. When this got a laugh he decided he could eat the car too. He could eat the tires and engine and bumpers. He was about to devour the trees and road when we called a halt—suggesting that he might spoil his appetite for the turkey.

However, we had a deeply impressive experience awaiting us along that road home, one that made us forget even our Christmas dinner—for a while.

XII

AN INDIAN'S CHRISTMAS

WE HEADED down the snow-walled road toward home. Ray was driving, Ada and Hi-Bub sharing the front seat with him. Giny and I were in the rear seat. Conversation was happy, snappy and mostly about the coming dinner.

At a point about two miles from our destination we rounded a curve and discovered a man a short distance ahead walking in the same direction we were going. He was an impressive figure, straight, tall, powerful, with an easy gait that was covering ground at a remarkable speed. As we drew nearer we could see that he wore a coonskin cap and a buckskin jacket with a woolen shirt beneath. He had ankle-high shoes with trousers rolled to the tops, lumberjack fashion. He wore wood-chopper mittens and carried a packsack on his back.

"Who would that be, walking on a day like this?" asked Ada, studying the man intently.

"I believe I know," said Ray, slowing down. "There's only one man in this country who can walk that fast—*Big John Shawano, the Indian.*"

Hi-Bub nearly jumped through the windshield.

"John Shawano?" questioned Ada. "Why, he's supposed to be about a hundred years old!"

113

"Yes," replied Ray. "No doubt he's walking to his cabin. It's easily fifteen miles from here. Maybe he has been in town."

We stared at the stalwart figure, now very close to us. It was Big John Shawano. The temperature then was near the zero mark. The loose snow of the roadway made difficult walking. Yet this remarkable old Indian had already walked five miles from town, and he was fearlessly facing fifteen miles more.

"We have time, haven't we, to give Big John a lift?" asked Ray, who has never been known to neglect anyone in need of aid. "What do we care if dinner is late? Let's take him home."

We all agreed quickly, and Hi-Bub spilled "yeth's" all over the car as he jumped up and down excitedly.

Ray touched the horn as we approached the man. He did not look around, but merely stepped to one side, thinking a car wanted to pass. There was not the slightest move on his part to gain a lift. Ray stopped beside him, rolled down a window and called, "Hello, there, John, where are you going?"

Big John halted and looked at us almost defiantly. He did not smile, though his stern look softened as he recognized Ray and me. "Oh—you!" he said in a deep voice. "Me go home!"

"Hop in with us and we'll take you there," Ray continued.

"Yes, come on, John," I added to the invitation. "Climb in." I opened the car door.

John looked at us with a stolid expression. "No want

ride," he said briefly. "John got these—they good!" He pointed to his long legs.

"But it's cold, John," persisted Ray. "We can have you home in a few minutes."

"John no stand still," grunted the Indian obstinately. "He walk—no get cold. No hurry. Got big time."

"But, John," Ray argued, "this car is nice and warm. We have a heater in it. You can go home comfortably."

John didn't budge. I never had a more difficult job of picking up a hitchhiker than we now encountered. In grunty talk mixed with pantomime, the proud old chieftain made us understand that tomorrow he would have no car but he would still have his legs. If he got used to the car, maybe he would wish for one, and he knew he couldn't have such a thing. But he could have his legs. He had had them for a long time and expected to keep them. Tomorrow he would still travel that way and he wanted to be satisfied to do so.

We were almost outtalked by the immovable Indian. The car was getting cold from the open door and we had about decided to let him finish his trip on foot without further argument from us.

Then suddenly John changed the whole course of the conversation himself. His dark eyes lighted up under influence of an idea.

"You read?" he asked of me, taking hold of the door to prevent me from shutting it.

"Read?" I repeated, wondering at the question. "Why, yes, John, I can read. Why do you ask?"

"Me no read!" said John. He drew himself up proudly

as he added, "John know sky, he know trees, he know birds, deer—now he want read!"

"What do you want to read, John?" asked Giny, understanding the trend of the Indian's talk. "Do you have a letter or something you want us to read for you?"

John had already thrown off his packsack and was fumbling through it. Presently he brought out a newly acquired book, still wrapped up. He handed it to me.

"You read him!" he commanded with chiefly authority.

I unwrapped the book and we were all surprised to see a copy of the Bible.

"Why, John," I exclaimed, "it would take days to read this to you. This is the Bible."

"Me know," said Big John impatiently. There was a moment of silence as the Indian searched in his limited English vocabulary for the right words. Then he leaned forward, touched the book and asked, "Him—him—tell—the story?"

We were getting some idea of what he wanted. "You mean the story of Christ, John?" I asked. "Yes, it is in here. Would like me to tell it to you?"

"No!" The Indian's answer was so sharp and explosive it startled us. *"No!* Me hear story plenty time. Man tell John. Woman tell John. Father tell John." He measured off various heights from the ground with his hand, indicating that he had been told the story of Jesus from his childhood to the present. "How I know they tell truth?" he asked strongly. "Now John want read! What he say?" And he nearly knocked the book out of my hand with emphatic pointing. Apparently he was confident

that the Bible contained the truth, and he wanted this story directly from its sacred pages.

I had been fingering through the book. It was a splendid edition bound in limp leather. John had obtained the best he could get.

"I'll tell you what we'll do, John," said Giny. "You let us drive you home and we will read the story of Jesus as we go. What do you say?"

John did not feel it necessary to say anything. His kind never use words when actions will do. That was the pattern of John Shawano's world. Nature deals with action, not talk, and Nature was John's environment. By the time Giny had finished her suggestion, he had placed his packsack on the car floor and climbed in. He sat on the edge of the seat as if he expected to leave any moment. He was so tall his coonskin cap brushed the top of the car.

It was then that I stole a look at Hi-Bub. We had been so intent on our conversation that we had forgotten about the youngster, now on his knees looking over the back of the front seat. He looked as if he had just swallowed a stick of dynamite. It seemed that if one more stirring and exciting thing happened, it would set off an explosion. His eyes were as wide open as the sockets would permit. He breathed heavily through his mouth as if he had been running uphill. Here was Big John Shawano, a real live Indian chief, right where he could touch him! It was almost too much.

"John," I said, as Ray got the car under way again. "Before I start reading I wonder if you would mind shaking hands with a friend who has known of you and admired you a lot. This is Hi-Bub."

The old Indian looked at Hi-Bub severely. Hi-Bub cringed a bit. Then I noticed a little smile creep into John's eyes, though his lips remained fixed. Suddenly he extended his hand toward Hi-Bub, with an explosive *"How!"*

Hi-Bub would have tumbled over backward had not Ada caught him. Timidly he put his hand in Big John's great hardened palm. He made several attempts before he succeeded, but finally he stuttered out a faint "H-h-h-how."

"Good boy," said John firmly. "He grow big—strong—carry much—walk far."

"Ye-ye-ye-yeth," said Hi-Bub.

"John," I said, feeling freer now that the Indian showed some understanding of our boy. "Do you know of an Indian boy living in the woods whose name is Little John Deer Foot?" My question was accompanied by a wink.

John looked at me, then at Hi-Bub. "Like him?" he said.

"Yes, something like Hi-Bub," I affirmed. "Hi-Bub knows him and I thought maybe you would too."

"Yes—me know Little John," said the old chieftain, with no change of expression. "Good boy. He come some-time—live at Big John's cabin. You like him?"

Hi-Bub could only nod. This adventure had gone beyond words.

Big John Shawano had enough of this child's play now, however. His eyes narrowed, and the muscles of his fine bronze face twitched. For a few moments under the influence of Hi-Bub we had seen into his heart and found him capable of tender thoughts. Now the habitual look of austerity returned to his countenance. Again he was the chieftain. His tone was nothing short of imperious as he said to me: *"Read."*

I was seeking the right place. In the meantime Giny tried to enter into a pleasant conversation with our strange guest. "Do you have any of your people coming to spend Christmas with you, John?" she asked.

"No!" said John with a wave of his hand. "Read!"

Giny's ever-ready sympathy was stirred. "Oh, you shouldn't be alone on Christmas, John. You could go to your people——"

The old Indian raised his hand to silence her. His eyes flashed impatience. "Me—lone? he asked, as if the suggestion were ridiculous. "Me no lone! Me never lone!" He straightened to his full height. "God with John," he said in loud tones. "God with John day, night, all time."

"Oh," said Giny. We all felt there was nothing more to say on that subject.

I had turned to the second chapter of Luke now and began reading the story of the first Christmas. We were fascinated by the reactions of the old Indian. He seemed to have forgotten we were there. His attention was fixed on the "Big Book," as he called the Bible. It took much explaining and rereading to reach his thought with the story, but he grasped it amazingly well. The events could not have been more real and vivid for him had they been happening that hour. His austerity disappeared. His eyes sparkled with happiness. Several times he laughed aloud. I had to repeat to him how Jesus was laid in a manger "because there was no room . . . in the inn." He wanted to hear again and again how the wise men came to worship the newborn babe. "They wise," said John. "They know papoose is son of God. People in wigwam—" we found he meant the people who were at the inn when Jesus was born—"people in wigwam, they not know. They no make room for papoose. Bah!"

We were understanding him better too, particularly his gestures. He told how his father, a chief well known in the early days of Wisconsin, had taught him of Jesus and Christianity. John did not go to any church. With a sweep of his hand he made it clear that the great forest, the earth and the heavens were his church. "All God!" he said, meaning creation. "John feel good. He know all God."

We realized he meant that he found God everywhere. When the birds sing he hears God. When dawn comes he sees God. When it is silent in the forest he feels God. "God make trees, flowers, lakes," said John. Then with a look of contempt he added, "White man think he smart—think he make world. Hah—I laugh!" He did laugh heartily.

"What papoose Jesus say?" suddenly asked John, touching the Bible with his finger. "He teach. What he say?"

Some of the sacred sayings of Jesus were read to him. There was the account of the Sermon on the Mount, the

Last Supper, and the story of the Resurrection and the Ascension.

John listened closely. He closed his eyes for a few minutes' thought. Then through the medium of broken English and vivid gestures he delivered a sermon that we will never forget. His convictions were absolute. Jesus had told men how to live, the old Indian said, but they "no listen." He had taught them to be kind, to love one another. They didn't listen. Jesus taught them about God, but they wanted to think only of money, wine and meanness.

"Men listen Jesus—they be happy," he said, with a sweep of his arm that barely missed striking Ada in the face. "They no fight, make no war, no be sick—they not use *big boom!*" We learned that "big boom" was the atomic bomb, of which John had heard. By impressive gestures he told how destructive the big boom would be. One might drop here, and there would be no more trees, no lakes, no flowers—just a big hole. "White man better listen Jesus quick," said John. "Maybe too late. Big boom come—no men left."

Our reading and talking continued until we arrived at the trail that led for a mile back to John's woodland cabin. We could see the tracks he had made as he came out before dawn that morning—to walk twenty miles to town, pick up the Bible which a friend had obtained for him and walk home again.

John was still deep in the story about Jesus when he stepped out of the car and shouldered his packsack. He shook his head in disapproval of the world. "Papoose tell men how be happy," he declared. "He tell them how be well—how live long—tell about God." Here he paused for a moment, and a complete change of expression came over him. He fairly shouted, "White man nail him up!" His eyes flashed and he raised his fists above his head. For an instant he was the warrior. Hi-Bub crawled into Ray's lap. We felt that if Big John Shawano had been there, the Crucifixion would never have occurred.

The Indian took his leave of us with never an expression of thanks. The ride had meant nothing to him. He was thinking of what had been read. "This papoose birthday," he said finally. "Big John happy. John talk with God all day."

Without another word he turned and went down the trail, his powerful strides sending the snow spraying before him. We called good-by, but he did not reply. We watched him until he disappeared into a clump of balsam trees. Then Ray turned the car about and we headed for home.

"I don't know just what he said or did to impress me so much," said Giny, voicing a thought we all had. "I have a clearer sense of what Christmas really means than I had before."

Hi-Bub finally found his tongue. "Oh boy—Big John is a *thwell* Indian," he said.

We had our old-fashioned Christmas dinner. June had tended the turkey perfectly. She and Hi-Bub sat together at the table as they had planned. At our suggestion he asked the blessing, saying, "Thankth, dear God, for all thith nith food—Tham Cammel, may I have the gith-ard?"

It was a wonderful dinner and a wonderful evening that followed, filled with songs, presents and good will. However, there was a richness and solemnity to it all that we hadn't anticipated. The spirit of fun was there, but in addition we had the feeling of the meaning of the day. That was the gift of our meeting with Big John Shawano. Several times we recalled the last sight we had of him striding back alone to his simple woodland cabin deep in the forest saying, "This papoose birthday. . . . Big John happy. . . . John with God all day."

Hi-Bub's daddy called for him at the appointed hour. At first the lad didn't want to go. It was hard to leave the scene of so much fun. June saved what might have been a small rebellion by saying, "Hi-Bub—I must go to bed now. Good night. Please come to see me again, won't you?"

A fellow would just have to go home and dwell on that—and Hi-Bub did.

XIII

ICY RECEPTION

IT WAS early April when we next saw our Sanctuary. Winter had departed, but it had left some of its belongings. On the north side of hills and in protected places there were remnants of snow.

· Most impeding to our progress was the cold fact that ice still ruled the lakes. The ice was at the stage where it was too thin to bear our weight, yet so thick no boat could plow through it. Along the shores there was a channel of open water about ten feet wide, while the rest of the surface was monopolized by this huge field of floating ice that weighed thousands of tons.

Giny and I felt a bit disheartened as we stood at the end of the road on the shore of the lake which adjoins ours. Our boat had been left here. A twenty-minute row, if one could row, would carry us through a channel, around a point to our island.

We were anxious to reach our home. Since the Christmas visit our days had been filled with intense travel and activity. Now we wanted to be at our cabin to watch the coming of spring. We had been tempting ourselves with thoughts of the cool, quiet, long evenings we would have before the fireplace. There would be time to read and think. Many of our woods friends would be there. Ah—

that was the point that gripped us. Our hearts were eager to know which of these creatures were still around and whether they remembered us.

It was this anxiety that impelled me to do a very foolish thing. We had stopped to see Ray, Ada and June, and they had begged us to make no attempt to reach our island until the ice was gone. They invited us to stay with them for the day or days that this might require—how long no one could know for sure. We planned to accept their hospitality, but decided to drive on to the end of the road and look the situation over. Hi-Bub was still in school, a fact for which I am grateful, otherwise he might have been invited along to share in the hazardous experience that followed. What happened furnished material for nightmares for a long time to come.

As we stood looking out across the ice floe a great crack developed, running from the place where we were to the channel leading to our lake. In a few minutes this had become an open thoroughfare about three feet wide. We watched it anxiously. If we could get through that route into our lake, it seemed certain that we could follow along close to the shore until we reached the island. Once there it would make no difference to us how long the ice held on. We had adequate supplies for many days.

To be ready for any opportunity I brought our boat to the water's edge. We kept eying the action of the ice. The channel was still widening. It took on the appearance of a fair-sized river, wide enough to permit free use of oars. I estimated that in five minutes we could get through it and reach the channel into our lake. The idea did not seem quite right, but that was where impatience gave the final push toward wrong decision. "Let's go!" I exclaimed. I charge myself with full responsibility for what followed. Giny was inexperienced with ice floes. However, I had seen them before and knew the crushing power in their tremendous weight. Moving in even a gentle drift, such ice fields are capable of crushing boats, piers, boathouses and of moving concrete pilings.

Quickly we pushed our boat into the water and loaded it with the most important of our luggage and supplies. Not thoroughly convinced of the wisdom of the move, I did think to put into the boat a long iron pipe and a mattock that were in the garage.

We started through the open water, and I rowed with all my strength. We had to get through that channel while the great ice fields remained separated. Everything was going splendidly until we had covered about half the distance. Then we felt a strong gust of wind blow up suddenly.

"Sam, look ahead!" cried Giny.

I did, and what I saw gave me no pleasure. The wind was causing the ice floes to drift together again. The river of open water was closing ominously. In an instant I realized the situation we were in. It was useless to try to return. Our only chance was to go ahead. I pulled desperately at the oars and the boat lunged forward, but obviously it was too late. We could not possibly get through before the gap closed. Our boat would be crushed like an eggshell. Already the channel had narrowed until my oars were striking ice on either side. Giny and I shifted our positions and used the oars as paddles so we could stroke close to the boat. Soon the ice was so close that even this method of paddling was impossible.

"We must try the mattock, Giny," I exclaimed, when I realized that the oars were now useless.

"And with every stroke—a prayer," she added in calm tones. I looked up to see her smiling so fearlessly that I paused an instant to be grateful for such a companion.

In my life in the forest I have often been in circumstances demanding my last ounce of strength. Nature is that way, and there is a rough, strong joy about it. This situation called for all the stamina I had—and made me borrow some. It was necessary for me to keep breaking off large cakes of ice from the margin of the floes that pressed on us from either side so that the crushing power was kept from the boat. I joked about "Crossington washing the Delaware," and managed to grunt that "Old Charley did this," but there was very little humor in my

thought. We were in a position that was just plain tough.

As pieces of ice were broken loose, we forced them down under the edge of the floes. This cleared a few inches of water at a time so we could move forward with the boat. But the gains were slight and the distance we must travel relatively great. I dared not pause for a moment. The mattock had to be swinging constantly, or the ice would close in on us. Once the channel did close completely under the bow, lifting the front of the boat into the air. It looked as if we were defeated. Then with the long iron pipe I was able to reach ahead, break loose a large cake and let us down into free water again.

We were saved at another point by Giny's thoughtfulness. She saw that my hands were tiring and my grip on the mattock was not very firm. At her suggestion we tied a rope firmly about the handle of the mattock. It was less than five minutes later when the invaluable tool flew from my hands into the water beneath the ice floe. By aid of the rope we pulled it back quickly and the chopping went on.

How long this battle continued we do not know. Probably it was about three hours, though it seemed much longer than that. Before the end came I had lost all sense of personal strength. My shoulder, arm and back muscles ached severely from the strain. The chopping had to be done in a most awkward way, as I had to reach out from the side of the boat to cut the ice at the greatest possible distance. Every blow must be strong, for the ice was about two feet thick—though fortunately somewhat softened from the spring sunshine and rains.

Surely there is a great reservoir of spiritual power into

which faith may dip when the frail and faulty human source is exhausted. Throughout history men have found this to be true. "Man's extremity is God's opportunity."

At one time I felt as if I could not carry on. My feeling of weakness had reached the point where my blows were losing the necessary power. I looked ahead at the long stretch of ice yet to be conquered. It seemed hopeless. Then came to my thought something my sweet mother had once said to me: "The tremendous strength of Jesus was explained when he said, 'I can of mine own self do nothing' . . . and again, 'the Father that dwelleth in me, he doeth the works.' " She pointed out that "he recognized that all real power is God." Such nuggets of inspiration are a priceless heritage. Recollection of this came as I realized that I was now at that point—*I could do nothing.* In my heart I prayed, trusting my mother's words.

Now a sound caught our attention—a voice from the skies. "Sam!" cried Giny. "Hear that precious little creature. It is he—and he has discovered us."

"Cheer, cheer, cheer!" came the call from a little feathered object that was winging directly toward us. "Congare-e-e-e-e—Congare-e-e-e-e!" went the happy song. There was Cheer, the red-winged blackbird! The last to leave us in the autumn, the first to return in the spring. He circled about us, sometimes fluttering like a helicopter close over our heads. His joy at finding us was unmistakable. I am sure he would have alighted on the boat itself except for the activity that was going on there. The mattock was swinging again. This bit of good cheer was the mental medicine I needed. The blows of my pick grew stronger—"of strength not my own." The ice broke off in increasingly large chunks. I thought no more of myself but felt an exhilaration in the battle. There was really a wild joy about it.

When at last we slid into the calm open water at the far side of the ice floe, I sank exhausted to the bottom of the boat. Giny uttered a prayer of gratitude for that reserve strength which had come to carry us through. Back of us we could see the path we had cut outlined by floating cakes of ice that were now being ground to pieces. For days afterward my thought reviewed that adventure. Often I dwelt on the tragic end it might have had if I had failed to continue swinging that mattock. The loss of a single blow might have meant the losing of the battle. And I knew that the endurance which carried us through was not in my muscles, but came directly from the Source of all creation.

When we had rested for a time and I could lift the oars once more, we rowed on. Our path was easy now. In our own lake we stayed close to shore where it was ice-free. When we rounded the last point of land we were overjoyed to find the region about our island entirely open.

"You blessed little home!" said Giny as we walked up to our door. "You know how we love you when we will go through an experience like that to get here."

Cheer was not long in joining us. He came singing as usual. He lighted at our feet and strutted around in that funny little way of his, spreading his wings and turning his head from side to side. How he loved the feast of peanut crumbs we gave him!

"It's all right, old top," I said to him. "After what you did for me today I will buy you enough peanuts to fill this house—if you want them."

A few crumbs were enough, however. Then Cheer flew away, perhaps to survey home-building sites for later use. He was the only one of our wildwood friends who put in an appearance those first hours.

Evening came with heavenly calm. We ate our dinner before a grate fire that warmed our spirits as well as our bodies. Presently we heard someone calling our names.

"What ho—Campbells!"

We went outside to listen. It was Ray's voice, coming from the far shore, fully half a mile away.

"Hello, Ray!" we called in unison.

"Are you all right?" came the question.

"Yes, we're all right," we called back, spacing our words so they could be understood.

"I saw your path through the ice," he called. "Came out to see if anything was wrong."

He would! Ray seems to have been put in the world just to do thoughtful, helpful things for others. It had been a long hike for him to the place where he could call to us.

"Thanks," I yelled. "We got through all right." I saved the story for a time when we would be closer together, for I knew Ray understood that no one went through ice that way without a struggle.

"You did a good job," he called back.

However, I felt no pride in what had been done, but rather a chagrin that I had attempted it. It had been a lesson in the folly of impatience—and a severe one.

XIV

LOOK WHO'S HERE!

FOR TWO days the ice kept us marooned on the island. The weather was still and cool, and it looked as if the great gray ice floe meant to stay in the lake all summer.

It made no difference to us now, however. This period of isolation gave us time to set our cabin in living order, and to take inventory of our forest friends.

Cheer, of course, was the very first one to report. He was back again at dawn of our first day on the island. He was back every hour all through the day too. As far as we could tell, there was not another blackbird on the lake as yet. Again, one has to be careful not to claim too much in experiences with animals, for after all we can have only opinions about them. However, we felt that our friendship had become a strong influence in Cheer's life, that caused him to face hazards of weather and seasons to be near us longer.

In those early hours the first morning it seemed as if the forest was opening a series of little trap doors to release one creature after another. Stubby, the chipmunk Hi-Bub loved so much, came bounding right up to the screen door. Not knowing the art of knocking, he ran up and down the screen until I went out to greet him—and pay the fee in peanuts. Beggar Boy, the other veteran chipmunk, came up to pay his respects and be paid. Then Still-Mo, the red squirrel with the bushy tail, came racing to the cabin, sending the chipmunks toward the horizons.

"Still-Mo!" Giny cried as we recognized the little animal. "Are we glad to see you!" It really was quite an experience. This chickaree had disappeared toward the end of the previous autumn. We had feared she might have suffered one of the tragedies common to forest folk. Here she was back again, however, as lively and as belligerent as ever.

Blooey, the old blue jay, was on hand. He identified himself by catching a peanut we tossed into the air. It always amazes us how these creatures retain memories of their little characteristic stunts. Blooey knew the very tree limb he had perched on when begging for handouts. He knew the rhythm of the event. I would stand near him and count "one, two, three," making motions to toss a peanut at each count. On the first two motions he would merely flutter his wings, but at the word *three,* he would take to the air to meet the peanut and catch it firmly in his beak. It was now six months since he had gone through this routine. Yet, at first sight of us he recalled it all and executed his part of the act as perfectly as if it had been going on daily.

The same was true of Still-Mo. Where the tiny animal had been during the elapsed months no one could know. It was a safe presumption, however, that she had been through trying experiences, the kind that might erase memories of her habits at the Sanctuary. But it was as if she had never been away. One of her cute tricks was to

tease Giny. Giny is a soft object for such teasing anyway, as she loves these little creatures so much that she is always wanting to do something for them. Still-Mo had figured out a route whereby she could climb to the kitchen window and appear directly in front of Giny's work table. Whenever there were pies, cakes, cookies or other culinary products in the making, Still-Mo made the most of it. She

would climb to the window and look in at Giny with the
most appealing and pathetic expression. One would think
she was on the verge of starvation. Giny could never re-
fuse her. She would stop her work and walk toward the
cabin door. Still-Mo knew the move. Down she would
go, and when Giny opened the door there would be the
red squirrel to meet her. Usually Giny placed a handful
of nuts on the doorstep to keep the energetic chickaree
busy for a few minutes. The nuts would be quickly disposed of and then—back to the kitchen window would
come Still-Mo to put on the sob act again. Now nearly a
year had passed since this had been done. Yet, while Giny
worked at the first breakfast, at the kitchen window appeared the pathetic face of Still-Mo. Of course Giny's
heart melted. When she walked to the front door, there
was Still-Mo waiting for the expected donation.

Next came Nuisance, now a very powerful red squirrel.
We were much pleased at his coming, for I believe Hi-
Bub would have been a sad little boy if his beloved "Noothanth" had not returned. Still-Mo did not welcome him
as much as we did, however. They engaged in a rough and
tumble fight that ended only when each ran away from
the other. They perched on stumps a few feet apart and
for a long time bored holes in the still atmosphere with
the sharp, scolding "chickare-e-e-e." Nothing can sound
saucier than a red squirrel, and when they are addressing
one another their tongues are sharpest.

We walked around the island to see how our trees had
endured the winter. All were in good shape except one

white pine. It had some markings that made us stop and examine it closely. No question of it; a porcupine had peeled the bark halfway down the tree. It gave us a thrill to see it. Not that we like to lose a tree, but this indicated the probable presence of a porcupine on the island. Could it be one or more of those we had known as pets?

When we were returning to the cabin, Giny suddenly caught my arm. "Look! Look! Look!" she exclaimed. It was a sight that gladdened my heart. Peering out at us from under a shed were four homely faces with shoe-button eyes, cupped ears and dirt-covered noses.

"It's our woodchucks—our little Sausages!" exclaimed Giny excitedly.

Instantly the four little faces disappeared, only to reappear and look us over as if they couldn't believe their eyes. Then encouraged by our entreaties and tender greetings they began advancing toward us in spurts. Once convinced that their memories were not playing them false, and that we were the people they had known before their long hibernation began the previous September, they came to us unhesitatingly.

Six little sausages had gone to sleep in the autumn. We had named them Thuringer, Bratwurst, Salami, Wiener, Patty and O. Bologna. Four now returned to greet us in the spring. That is a good average. The story of the other two would have to be left in the deeply secret diary of Nature. We were sure of the identification of Patty only. Since his babyhood he had some odd mannerisms not shared by the others. Now we could recognize these traits.

His size distinguished him too. He was the runt of the family and although this spring he was a full-grown woodchuck he was still small for his kind.

In the late afternoon came another surprising experience. Giny glanced out the front door and there near our step stood a huge mink. She called me to look at him. He was really a graceful and beautiful creature, for all his bad reputation as a killer. Standing there he looked so peaceful it was hard to believe he was one of the most bloodthirsty of all predators. Our chipmunks and red squirrels had discovered him, but they spent no time in admiring his beauty as we did. They chirped and chattered a warning to the whole woods that a dangerous enemy was at hand.

We decided the visitor must be driven from the island. While I know that predators are necessary in the balance of nature, the friendliness of our island creatures is so valuable to us we cannot permit them to be harmed. Yet I did not want to destroy this invader, for he belongs to nature's scheme. I stepped out of the door to invite him to leave. He looked up at me calmly, moved a few feet and stopped. Not the slightest bit of fear was in evidence. I walked toward him. He gave ground reluctantly, looking at me with puzzled defiance. Apparently he had not expected to see people in this ice-bound country. I picked up a stout stick and beat the ground with it, shouting as I did. He walked away, though there was nothing panicky in his movements. I followed him at a short distance. He stopped and turned around fearlessly to face me. Think of the courage of the rascal. I speak of him as being a large mink, yet he would not have equaled in size a house cat. But there he stood looking at me as though he would just as soon fight as not. I stopped too, beat the ground and shouted until he took a notion to move on. That much noise would have sent a bear away at a gallop. Not this fellow. Had I pressed him harder I believe he would have attacked me.

We continued our little game until the animal reached the edge of the water near our boathouse. He paused for a moment there looking at me as much as to say, "I'm going, mister, but don't get any idea you're chasing me away." I waited patiently for him to take his leave in his own way, admiring his courage the while. I felt definitely attracted to the dachshund-shaped creature. It seemed as if the difference between us might be easily settled and a friendship established.

However, our interests in the forest were too much at variance. I beat the ground once more, insisting that he go. He inched into the icy water, then swam away smoothly and rapidly. I watched him as he skirted the edge of a great ice cake and made his way to the mainland.

"Learn to live on peanuts and then come back to us!" I called after him. However, I fancy his diet remained the same as it had been heretofore. We saw no more of him.

As evening approached came the most precious experience of the day. We saw a solemn, slow old porcupine coming down the path. No doubt it was his sharp, amber-colored teeth that had stripped the bark from our tree. But who was he? Was this a stranger who had discovered our island during the winter and found it a safe and satisfying place to live? Or was it one of our pets? We realized it couldn't be Inky, the first one of these strange creatures whose friendship we had gained. Inky when last seen had been much larger than this one. However, the animal was the right size for either Salt or Pepper, the two we had raised together.

We walked to meet the slow-moving creature. He discovered us and stopped short. We watched closely, for only by his actions could we learn his identity. Would he remember us and, like Still-Mo, recall certain stunts that would tell us his name? It was not so easy this time. This porcupine kept us guessing. At first he seemed actually frightened, and raised his quills. Giny gave the porcupine call. She talked to him in the manner and tones used with our porcupine pets when they were babies. I called in my most reassuring manner too. All this had an effect on the old fellow. He stopped and faced about. His quills went flat to his back. He regarded us closely as if he were trying to understand.

We began to feel sure that this was one of our pets. We reasoned it was most likely Salt. Pepper was not such a mild creature. Certainly a wild porcupine who had never had friendly contact with people would not behave as this one was doing. He rose on his hind legs and stretched his nose toward us, still trying to understand. Giny bent over him. Their faces were not over a foot apart. Still the porcupine showed no alarm.

"Let's try the peanut test," I suggested in a whisper. Since peanuts are not native to the region, it was certain that a wild porky would have no taste for them. On the other hand our pet porcupines had been very fond of them. I shelled one and handed a kernel to Giny. She held it out until it touched the porcupine's nose. This was too much for him as things now stood. Apparently his memory of us and the place was not clear as yet. When he was touched he let out a little squeal. Immediately his wild instincts came to the fore. He whirled about, quills rising. Away he went through the brush. Soon we heard him scratching the bark of a tree as he climbed to a place he regarded as safe.

"He can't fool me, though," declared Giny as we returned to the cabin. "That is Salt. We may have to prove to him who he is, but there's no doubt in my mind."

It was clear to us that moment that one of the first tasks of the season at the Sanctuary would be to get this old creature to recall fully his friendship with us.

During the morning of the third day we saw the ice break up and disappear from our lake. It was a thrilling sight. The whole ice field began rocking under the pressure of a high wind. The motion seemed gentle at first, but surely there were stupendous forces and masses at work. Great cracks appeared. These spread into rivers like the one through which we had gone on the eventful day of our arrival. Then the massive pieces of ice came together again. The action was slow and the collision seemed to be gentle, yet where the edges touched there were mounds of white ice shavings rising like huge snow drifts. Again there would be new cracks, new rivers and then fresh collisions. The wind increased its strength and a warm sun shone down. The process was a quick one. We would never have thought it possible, but within three hours not a pound of ice was left in the lake. The last scene was of a few floating flat-topped icebergs being buffeted by waves. These dissolved as quickly as if they had been made of sugar, and the lake was ready for summer.

With the coming of night the mystical calm which is the poetic mood of Nature returned. No camera can record it, no artist catch the fullness of its heavenly charm, no words describe it, nor can thought fully rise to appreciation of its glory. We built a campfire and sat attentive to its tongues of flames as if they spoke a language pure enough to delve into such celestial things.

Then out of the dark draperies that spread over woods and waters came a canoe, announced only by the soft dipping of its paddles. Ray, Ada and June had come to join us for the evening. The spirit of friendship which attended their arrival was needed in the perfection of the evening. Remember the words of Cowper?

> How sweet, how passing sweet, is solitude!
> But grant me still a friend in my retreat,
> Whom I may whisper, Solitude is sweet.

We talked little, for there seemed to be nothing to say that would add to the grandeur of the silent universe. Occasionally we sang a song in muted tones. Then when the midnight hour was near and there arose loud and clear the call of old Meph the wolf Giny said, "That does it! His wild call was all that was needed to make this complete."

XV

DOG MEETS PORCUPINE

THE DAY came when Hi-Bub made his first visit of the season. It was good to have him around again. In a way he was like the forest creatures we had been greeting— he picked up his life at the Sanctuary as if there had never been an interruption. We had barely finished our greetings until he was going about the island calling the names of his pets. They came running or flying to him, just as they had before a winter stepped between them.

There was a new problem relative to his companionship with these animals, however. Hi-Bub had brought Hobo along. Giny and I had not favored this. Through the years we found it best to keep dogs away from the Sanctuary. The creatures that have given us their confidence are at a disadvantage with a dog, and no doubt it is expecting a lot of even the most obedient dog not to chase them.

Hi-Bub pleaded the case for Hobo. He was sure his pet would obey. When he arrived at the island the first thing Hobo did was to take out after Still-Mo. He didn't get far with that frisky little creature. The red squirrel climbed a tree faster than Hobo could run along the ground, then sat telling the disappointed dog some uncomplimentary things about him and his ancestors. Hi-Bub caught up with his willful pet. He made the dog sit down

143

before him. This was not done by command. Hi-Bub
stood beside his pet and finally forced him into squatting
position by pushing with all his might, right where the
tail begins. Then the boy took hold of Hobo's ears so he
couldn't turn his head, and that way forced the dog to look
into his eyes.

"Lithen, Hobo," said the boy earnestly. "I told you a
million time-th not to chaith animalth. Now didn't I?"

Hobo's attention wandered, but Hi-Bub continued,
"You promithed me if I brought you here you would be
good. Didn't you now?"

Hobo spied a chipmunk a few feet away and tried to
get his head free, but Hi-Bub held him fast.

"Now, I'm gonna give you one more chanth," said the
youngster, his nose almost touching Hobo's. "If you are
bad again—well, you better hadn't!"

Either Hobo was impressed, or else he was awfully
comfortable right where he was sitting. As Hi-Bub
walked away, he didn't move a muscle.

I was noticing something about Hi-Bub that was somewhat disappointing to me. His lisp was disappearing. In
fact there was considerable difference in his speech since
I had first met him many months ago. Then one had to
listen closely to understand his words. Now, while the
lisp slipped in fairly often, it didn't come with its former
regularity. He even called me "Sam Cammel," with a
very clear hissing *s*. It is a foolish and unfair notion we
grownups have that leads us to want little ones to stay little
and to continue childhood ways. Such things as Hi-Bub's
lisp are so precious it is even hard to be philosophical

when they disappear. But I soon learned that the lisp was present in full force whenever Hi-Bub was excited.

"Tham Cammel, Tham Cammel," came his cry from somewhere back among the young balsam trees. "Come quick, Hobo won't th-top."

I rushed to the spot to find the dog digging frantically with his front feet, sending sand and gravel flying all over the place. Hi-Bub was tugging at his ears and scolding him, but making no impression.

"He'th after Patty Thauthage," cried Hi-Bub, much distressed. "Patty ran down thith hole. Th-top it, Hobo, th-top it, I tell you."

Hobo didn't stop until I picked him up and set him to one side. Then he kept his eye on that hole in the ground ready to make a dash for it the moment the pressure of my restraining hand ceased.

"Don't worry, he could never dig far enough to get Patty," I assured Hi-Bub. "It was a good thing Patty ran, though. I'm afraid you will have to give Hobo another scolding."

Hi-Bub did, in the conventional manner. He pushed down at the usual place and forced the dog into a sitting position. Then he took both ears as before and looked right into the dog's eyes as he delivered his reprimand. Again Hobo sat still as if much impressed. He gave a side glance at the hole in the ground, but since nothing was coming out of it he let it alone. Cheer, the redwing, came flying over, and lighted in a tree near Hi-Bub. Hobo looked up as much as to say, "If I only had wings I'd give you a run for your money too." He sat still, how-

ever, while Hi-Bub went on the run for peanuts to share
with Cheer.

I stood near Hobo so I could watch him. The funny
little mongrel amused me greatly. He had a mind of his
own, and he used it. He knew full well what was expected of him, but he didn't intend to be any more obedient than was absolutely necessary. With some object in
mind he got up and walked briskly for a few steps. Then
he discovered me watching him, and he sat down again. I
looked away as if I were paying no attention to him. He
got up and walked cautiously toward some bushes. When
I turned my head toward him, he sat down. Hi-Bub called
to me to come and see what Cheer was doing. I went, for-
getful of the dog. While we were both giving our full attention to the strutting and beautiful red-winged blackbird, there began suddenly a fierce scrambling through
the leaves accompanied by frantic squeaks and savage
barks. There went Stubby the chipmunk sailing through
the leaves, over logs, around rocks, with the wildly excited Hobo after him. Hi-Bub joined in the chase. I ran
after Hi-Bub. For a few minutes the island was in an up-
roar. Giny came out of the cabin to take part in our
frantic calling of "Hobo, Hobo!" Hobo yelped and
barked until he couldn't hear us—and he didn't want to
anyway. Stubby managed to keep ahead in the chase,
yelling frantically in his own way for the police, fire de-
partment and the national guard. The rumpus didn't end
until Stubby maneuvered into one of his underground re-
treats. Hobo promptly started another shower of sand and
gravel as he tried to follow the little creature into the

earth. I picked up the irate dog and set him to one side, rather forcefully I fear.

The expression on Hobo's face made Giny and me laugh in spite of our anger. He knew he had done something against our wishes, but his sorrow was only because he had been caught. When he glanced at us his ears fell flat to his head, and he wore a contrite expression. When he looked at the chipmunk hole, his ears stood up and he simply glared. He was breathing hard, and his tongue was hanging out till it nearly touched the ground. But he was not exhausted or sorry—he was just restrained, that was all.

Hi-Bub gave him another and more forceful lecture. I thought maybe the correction should be more severe, so I suggested we put Hobo in a large wire cage, where we had kept baby animals at various times. We tried this, but not for long. I didn't know so much noise could come out of anything the size of Hobo. He yelped, he barked, he whined, he howled. He caused everything on the island to start yelling too. The red squirrels sat in the trees above him and scolded their best. Chipmunks chirped at him. Blue jays screamed. Crows joined in the melee. Even Cheer abandoned his usual friendly attitude and uttered shrill cries at the irritating pup. Finally, for the peace of the community, we had to let him loose. Hi-Bub felt sure he would be a good dog now. "He feelth bad," said the boy. "I guess he doesn't know better."

Hobo did seem somewhat more agreeable now. He came up for our petting, acting as happy as if he were nobly forgiving us for all *he* had done.

I took Hi-Bub for a lesson in tree identification. He was really becoming a fine student. So far his interest in nature had been based on the fact that he loved it. He was sensitive to the beauty of the world, and certainly in sympathy with living things. Now to this he must add a knowledge of his surroundings lest the mere enthusiasm be insufficient.

"First, the pine trees," I said as we went on the trail to begin our study. "So many people think that all trees which have needles for leaves are pine trees. Most of such trees are evergreens, but pines are just part of the evergreen family."

"Uh huh," said Hi-Bub.

"Now there are three important pine trees in the northwoods," I went on.

"Thith northwoods?" said Hi-Bub.

"Yes."

"That's nice," he commented.

Then I pointed out specimens of the red, white and jack pines. He learned to know them by their long needles. The jack pine has two needles in each cluster, and so does the red pine. However, the needles of the red pine are longer and straighter than the jack pine's. I pointed out the flat scaly bark of the red pine.

"Now the white pine has five needles in a cluster," I said, indicating a small specimen of this important northwoods tree. "That is easy to remember," I continued. I held a cluster before him. "There is one needle for each letter in the word *white*."

"Huh?" said Hi-Bub.

"You know how to spell white, don't you?"

"W—h—i—t—e," he spelled carefully.

"That's right," I said. "There are five letters and here you see five needles in this cluster from the white pine. See, w-h-i-t-e." I emphasized the point by indicating a needle with each letter.

"Did the tree grow five needles just because it wuth a white pine?" asked Hi-Bub.

"No, Hi-Bub—it just happens that way," I said. "It helps us remember, doesn't it?"

"Remember what?"

"Why, remember what I just told you?"

"You mean how to spell white?"

"No, I mean how many needles a white pine has."

"Huh? How many does it have?"

"Why, five."

"Five what?"

"Needles—you know, leaves."

"Why?"

I don't know where this conversation would have ended if at that moment Hobo hadn't found a new way to get in trouble. We heard an explosion of yipes and barks not far ahead. Hi-Bub and I hastened to the scene of action. "Oh—I hope he isn't after Th-tubby again," mourned Hi-Bub as we approached the spot.

Hobo wasn't after Stubby. He had found a creature that wasn't so easily chased. We saw him a hundred yards ahead of us barking his best at a dark furry cluster not more than four feet from his nose.

"It'th a baby bear!" cried Hi-Bub.

"Oh, oh—I only wish it were," I exclaimed, realizing an awful truth. "Hobo, come here. Don't do that, you scamp, or you will be sorry."

"What ith it?" panted Hi-Bub.

"It is our porcupine, Hi-Bub," I declared. "See his quills? Hurry, we must save him."

"The porcupine?"

"No—Hobo!"

Hobo did not want to be saved. He saw us coming and undoubtedly remembered how we had spoiled his sport previously. This time he was going to get his job done before we reached him. He moved closer to the porky, barking more furiously.

It is generally known that a porcupine cannot shoot or throw his quills. However, I find few students of nature realize how quickly this strange animal can move, and how deadly is a blow from his needle-filled tail. Hobo didn't know this either. I tried my best to reach him in time, but I was too late. Right up to the porcupine he went, ready to sink his teeth in the creature. There was a sharp mixup during which the porky suddenly whirled and with his tail slapped Hobo right on the end of his nose. Such a cry of anguish I never heard from a dog before. All the fight was taken out of Hobo. With a nose full of those torturing quills he went slinking and howling through the brush. The old porcupine calmly climbed a tree and went to sleep.

I sought the disillusioned and suffering Hobo. No longer was he the cocky, chase-everything tyrant he had imagined himself to be when he arrived. He was a whim-

pering, pathetic little figure, head hanging low. Even his tail had lost its permanent wave.

"You are in for it, Hobo," I said as I took him up. "There's no way I can save you the punishment you brought on yourself."

"Tham Cammel," cried Hi-Bub, trying to pet his pal. "Tham Cammel, what do we do? What do we do?"

"We take the quills out, Hi-Bub," I said. "It isn't easy. We must take a pair of pliers and pull them out."

We cut the ends off the quills to let the air out of them. We also poured vinegar over them to soften them a bit. Yet even this doesn't help much. The quills of a porcupine are sharp as needles. They are barbed so that after they have entered the flesh it is difficult to withdraw them.

We all held Hobo as best we could. The poor pup realized we were doing our best for him. He yelped but he made no effort to run away. I pulled the spines out one at a time—one, two, three, four, five. . . .

"There is number six, Hobo," I said to the trembling creature. "Wish we didn't have to do this to you, but there is no other way. I wonder if you are honest enough to admit to yourself that you had this coming. Easy now, here is number seven."

"Yipe," cried Hobo.

"Sometimes, Hobo, before we learn better we let our conceit run away with us," I went on, reaching for the next quill with my pliers. "We think we are smart. You may be sure, Hobo, whether you are man or dog, if you think you are smart you are pretty dumb. It is the surest sign you aren't smart if you think you are. Steady now— here comes number eight."

"Yow-o-o-o-o-o-o!" went Hobo.

"The trouble is, when we think we are smart we imagine we have a right to chase and push other people around. We get mean and inconsiderate. That is the way you were today, Hobo. You were plain mean. You abused those that were smaller than you. You thought you were sort of a king and had a divine right to do as you pleased. Number nine."

"Yip, yip," moaned Hobo.

"You dogs are not the only ones who make that mistake, Hobo. Men and even nations do it. I am afraid I've done it too, though I know how wrong it is now. Sometimes boys with big muscles think they have a right to bully those who are not so strong. Sometimes girls with quick wit say mean things to those who aren't so sharp.

But, Hobo, no one gets away with it. The world isn't built that way. If one of us has more strength than another, it is so he can help the other—not bully him. Number ten."

"Yipe, yipe, yipe—oh-o-o-o-o-o-o-o," howled Hobo.

"Something always beats the bully, Hobo. You chased little chipmunks and squirrels that were smaller than you. Thought you were a big he-dog, I suppose. Thought you were brave and strong. You didn't realize it was a cowardly thing to do. Then along came a porcupine, someone that could handle you. He wasn't looking for trouble, but he could hand out plenty of it. When he struck you, you were whipped. Strange, God always has something like a porcupine in the way of a bully. Men bullies meet their matches, and they are slinking cowards when they do. Nations who try to bully the world meet their defeat too. And they howl just like you when punishment comes. Number eleven."

"Yow-o-o-o-o-o, yipe," cried Hobo.

"We ought to be good and decent in this world just for the sake of living rightly, Hobo—not because we are afraid we may bite the wrong thing and it will prove to be a porcupine. One way or another, we will be forced to do right. If we don't learn through a wish to be the way God made us, then we will be punished. Something stops us when we are on the wrong path. Number twelve."

"Arf, arf, arf," barked Hobo.

"After this you will have time to think. The world forgives a wrong very quickly—if we change our ways. We know what is right, don't we, old top? The way you looked up at me when I caught you chasing chipmunks showed you knew that was wrong. Well, if you want to live in a right way from now on, no one will remember this against you. But if you don't, you may be sure you will get into trouble again. Number thirteen."

Hobo used all his doggy vocabulary now. Thirteen porcupine quills buried deeply in the tender flesh about his nose! It was a severe lesson for Hobo. I believe he learned something through it. During the rest of his stay, he seemed to hesitate even to chase a fly off his tail.

As the time neared for Hi-Bub to return to his home, he said suddenly, "Oh, I forgot."

"You forgot what?" Giny asked.

"I forgot the letter."

"What letter?"

"This one," he said, drawing a much mussed envelope from his tiny pocket.

It was a letter from Tony's mother to Hi-Bub, sent with the request that he let us read it. Tony was doing nicely, she said. He was trying hard to be happy and to get well. "He would like a picture of Cheer," the letter ran. "I wonder if Mr. Campbell has one he could send. I feel sure Tony will be able to come to the northwoods this year if it won't be too much trouble for Mr. Campbell. It would be for only a week. If it is not convenient please do not hesitate to tell us. Tony won't be too disappointed. But if he may come it will mean so much to him."

Of course Tony would receive a picture of Cheer. We had one in natural color, showing the lovely bird with his wings beautifully spread.

"And you may tell Tony we want him to come, Hi-Bub," I said. "I expect it should be later in the summer when it is sure to be warm. I tell you what let's do," I said with sudden inspiration. "You come out when Tony does and stay right here so we can all have fun together. Will you ask your father and mother if you may do that?"

"They said yeth," replied Hi-Bub casually.

XVI

A BEAR'S HALLOWEEN

ONE OF those first days we went over to check up on Old
Charley, the cantankerous black bear. We found the bed
he had used for his hibernation. In the hollow of the overturned stump was evidence that he had been there for a
long time. Leaves and cedar bark were found in goodly
quantities pressed down by the weight of a heavy body.
We found samples of his black hair sticking to his bed.
However, Old Charley was not around, and he hadn't
been at this place for many days. Loose sand bore none
of his tracks. The bag of food we had left hanging from
a tree limb had been discovered, torn to shreds and its contents taken. No doubt that had been Old Charley's breakfast.

While we didn't see him, others did, and there was no
lack of news about him. On our trips to the village we
found the whole countryside buzzing with Old Charley
stories. That bear had launched himself out on an endless Halloween. The butcher, the baker, the candlestick
maker—as well as the garage man, postmaster, storekeeper
and banker all had grievances against our bear.

"How do they know it is Charley doing all this?" asked
Giny one day after we had been listening to tales of his
breaking into cabins, raiding clotheslines and frighten-

ing people. "Surely this might be the work of several bears."

"There's no mistake about it now," I answered. "I tried to defend him that way but it didn't work. Last year one bullet fired at him came pretty close to ending his career. It nipped off a large part of his left ear. Now he is known by that mark."

Anyway, Old Charley did things differently from other bears. He wasn't just in search of food, he was out to have a good time. A big, six-hundred-pound playboy—that was Old Charley.

We met some acquaintances in town who were in desperate frame of mind. They had just returned from a trout fishing trip—much earlier than was planned. Four of them had camped at a favorite spot along a fast-flowing stream. It was a secret haunt of theirs and for years they had gone there to open the trout season. Things went wonderfully well with them for a few hours. Trout were striking furiously. The breezes that blew across their camp carried tantalizing odors of frying fish, ham and bacon as well. They had the world to themselves. No one knew of their secret camping place—roads were far away and everything was heavenly. That is, until one morning when a big black bear stuck his head out of the brush on the stream bank opposite their camp and sniffed at the aroma coming from their savory breakfast.

At first the men were thrilled at the sight, then they were puzzled, and at last not a little disturbed. The bear acted strangely. He saw them but he wasn't frightened. He didn't run away, he just stayed there and sniffed. In fact, he surveyed the stream, looking for an easy crossing. His actions suggested that he would look with favor on an invitation to join the men at breakfast. They lacked hospitality, however, and showed this fact plainly. They shouted at him, cordially inviting him to go elsewhere. They beat on pans and threw rocks—but the bear simply stayed and sniffed.

"Maybe he can't hear us," suggested one of the men. "One of his ears is gone."

"He hears all right," said another, a bit discouraged. "He just doesn't care a hang."

The men were late getting to their fishing that morning, for the bear with one ear stood around watching them and, as one of them said, "A fellow doesn't feel like doing much when a bear is acting like that." At last Old Charley (it was he) disappeared into the brush and the men breathed more easily. There was the feeling, though, that they had not seen the last of the unwelcome visitor.

A few hours later two of them were wading and fly-fishing in some rapids, having very good luck, when suddenly out of the brush a short distance upstream came Old Charley. Nothing could ever convince those two men that the creature did not deliberately destroy their fishing. He was bent on being plain mean. He looked at them for a moment, then perhaps recalled their inhospitality of the morning. They told of the fiendish grin that came on his face and the flash of mischief in his eyes. Out into the stream he went about two good casts above them, beating the water with his huge paws, racing about the shallows in high glee, rolling and bathing, and in general doing

everything that would frighten a trout out from under its
dorsal fin!

The men stood and stared hopelessly. Old Charley
looked at them for a moment in merciless satisfaction,
then took up his capers with fresh energy. He was having
a wonderful time. The men waded ashore. It was the
wise and the only thing to do, for there were no more trout
in that rapids and there was a bear there. They couldn't
catch the one and didn't want to be caught by the other.
A few stones were thrown at the bear and a few uncomplimentary names called his way, but he paid no attention to
either. When he was sure the trout were scattered to the
far corners of the stream bed, Old Charley went bounding
away.

"He stopped long enough to give us the most insulting
grin I ever saw," one of the men declared. "Apparently
he was plumb tickled with what he had done."

That night the campers didn't have enough fish for a
full dinner, but they decided to cook up what they had and
finish the meal with bacon and eggs. One of the party was
elected to clean the few fish available. He went some distance from camp to a spot that had been used for the purpose before. He had forgotten his knife, and went back to
the tent to get it, leaving the fish on a log. When he returned, there sat Old Charley eating them, "smacking his
lips and grinning from the ear that wasn't there to the
one that was." The man's outburst of shouting brought
the others on the run. Then all of them stood helplessly
and watched their dinner consumed. Old Charley was in
his glory. Here was poetic justice. That morning they

had eaten breakfast while he looked on drooling. Now he was the gourmand, they the jealous spectators. In all his experience he had never obtained fish so easily. Usually he had to wait a long time beside a lake or stream until one swam close enough that he could snatch it and toss it up on shore with his paw. But these trout were already tossed up—plenty of them—and they were fresh.

The fishermen ate just bacon and eggs that night, while Old Charley probably curled up somewhere in the woods licking his chops in memory of his wonderful meal.

Relations between the campers and the renegade bear

became worse hourly. "That one-eared scoundrel set out to ruin our whole fishing trip—and he did it!" said one of the victims. There was no humor in his voice.

Charley became bolder and bolder, they said. The men waded the stream above and below the camp in an effort to carry on their fishing. But they were never in any one spot long before out of the brush would come their grinning heckler. Certainly Charley was determined that their catch should be reduced to a minimum. He would sail into the waters near them, beating and splashing about, chasing every swimming thing halfway to the ocean. "The only redeeming feature," commented one of the men who had retained a fragment of his sense of humor, "was to see the joy he got out of what he was doing. I couldn't help laughing at the hilarious way he acted, even if I was the victim."

Old Charley seemed to know intuitively where the fishermen would be. One day they would go upstream from the camp. Charley would be there. Then they would go downstream. He would be there too. Then they divided their party, two going upstream, two downstream, for they reasoned Charley couldn't be both places at once. This was good logic, and there was fine fishing that day. It was the last day in camp, however. In fact, there was very little camp left when they returned. Charley had chosen this time to call on them, and finding no one in the tent, he entered without knocking. Probably his woods diet had been a little monotonous, and he hankered for a change—say to *ham* or *bacon*.

The campers had taken the precaution of swinging a

packsack out of reach from the limb of a tree. But smoked meats had been around the tent long enough that everything smelled of them, and so Old Charley busied himself looking through everything. He did a job which, in the matter of thoroughness, would be a credit to the FBI. He broke into every pack and package in that tent, scattered the contents about the floor, ate what he liked and deliberately mistreated what he did not like. He hadn't quite finished his work when the men came back and interrupted him. Hence he had to depart in haste, for they were really mad now and one of them grabbed an ax. "Come on and fight like a man, you black so-and-so," shouted the frenzied fisherman, jumping up and down and waving his weapon. "I'll skin you alive!"

Charley surely thought the man meant it, and so he raced for the tall timber—dragging the entire tent with him for fifty yards!

After this, the men packed up and went home. Charley had literally chased them out of the woods. Had there been a gun in camp no doubt the bear's hide would have been stretched on someone's barn door, but this was not the hunting season and the men had no firearms.

"I'll know him if I ever see him again," declared the most irate of the fishermen. I think he was a little irritated by my smiles. "I'll shoot him loose from his other ear, so help me I will."

I could hardly blame him, yet I didn't want anything to happen to Old Charley. His wild and free spirit and his sense of humor—sadistic as it was—endeared him to our hearts. Really, I think the community loved him too, for though there were more threats against his life than ever were directed at Jesse James, the stories were told with a chuckle and there was a definite joy evident that the bear lived on. At least, it gave the people of the region material for conversation apart from the weather. I believe that in Old Charley many found a chance to live by proxy the kind of life most people want to live—wild, free of inhibitions, with a liberal mixture of joy and danger.

One story was told us by its victim, who showed unmistakable satisfaction that Charley lived on, even though he had made every effort to bring the bear's career to an end. At this man's farm near a main highway there was considerable stock. Cattle and horses were put out at pasture a half mile from the house. The farmer noticed that he was not getting so much milk as he expected and also that his horses were exceedingly tired and inefficient at their work. He tried a change of diet for his animals, but it had no effect.

Then he chanced to be down at his pasture late one night and noticed a strange thing. Cows and horses were galloping about wildly. It was no mere spasm of uncontrollable energy that caused them to run—*something* was chasing them. He hurried to the edge of the field where he could see better. With the aid of a full moon he was able to make out a huge dark form running in among his stock, keeping them constantly on the move. It was a bear!

Back to the house the farmer went, to return with his gun, for he feared the bear was striving to make a kill. He held his fire, however, because the animal was so close to the horses and cows that he could not get clear aim at him. Then he observed something extraordinary. The bear was not trying to catch the cows and horses. He would race after the animals and overtake them, but when this was accomplished he would turn his attention elsewhere and take out after other stock. Apparently his desire was just to keep them on the run. Never would he permit them to stand still. If a group pulled up in a corner of the field breathless and panting, he came on the double-quick to start them going again.

The farmer watched this for nearly an hour. Then he fired several shots into the air. Obviously the bear knew the meaning of this sound, for he disappeared into the darkness.

The next night he was back doing the same thing, and again the next and the next. He would not let those farm animals rest.

The farmer made every effort to get a shot at him. True, it was not hunting season, but there is no law on the statute books which says one must stand by and see his horses and cows play tag with a bear until they can't work or produce milk.

The game warden came to help corner this marauding bear. Once at dawn they caught a fairly good look at him. They could see plainly that one ear was missing—it was Old Charley.

Now the farmer was desperate. He didn't want to kill the bear, but something had to be done. Together with his neighbors he formed a posse. One night they placed themselves at convenient points so that the whole approach to the field was covered by waiting riflemen. They waited long and futilely. While they stood in silence to spring their ambush, they heard a wild noise arise from the pigs and chickens back near the house. It persisted so long that the farmer went to investigate. There went Old Charley racing away into the night, after giving the barnyard residents a chase they would never forget.

Then Charley, thoroughly successful and triumphant, visited this farm no more, while the community wondered where he would strike next.

There were other stories about Old Charley, plenty of them. Some were true, some were not, yet as in the previous autumn he was blamed for everything that was wrong. Giny was halfway between tears and laughter as we talked about him.

"Maybe the old fellow hears all this gossip and thinks he may as well do his best to be his worst," she commented, and added with concern, "He can't get away with it forever."

"Perhaps we could bribe him to stay back in the Sanctuary," I suggested. "If we kept enough of his favorite food near his old feeding station he might be content."

"It's worth a trial anyway," agreed Giny. "And it does seem to be the only thing we can do that offers any promise of forestalling a tragedy."

So plans were made to feed Old Charley out of the mess he had made for himself, and to prevent him from degenerating into a rug on someone's floor. His cafeteria where he had been released was to be put in service again, offering him everything from ham bones to honey—if only he would stay back in the woods and let people alone.

XVII

BOY NATURALIST

WE THOUGHT that we would have to bar Hobo from the Sanctuary after his first upsetting experience. As days went by we found ourselves little inclined to enforce the rule. Hi-Bub wanted his dog pal along with him. Furthermore we found that Hobo constituted an interesting experiment for us all.

Spring was well advanced when Hi-Bub brought his pet to the island once more. Giant bullfrogs were adding their voices to the twilight harmony. Twin flowers, marsh marigolds and wild lilies of the valley were in bloom. Shore lines were highlighted with the pure white blossoms of the shadbush, hilltops wore blankets of wild cherry blossoms.

Hi-Bub was taking his lessons in nature very seriously. He was imbued with a desire to learn. No longer was he satisfied with just his impression of the wonders about him. He questioned endlessly, sometimes irksomely.

It wasn't enough now to see the chipmunks disappear into the ground and be told that this hole was their home. He wanted to know how many rooms it had, if there was a basement, a bedroom, a dining room, a back door. Hence, with great labor, we dug into one of these remarkable subterranean dwellings. Unintentionally I selected an un-

usually large one for investigation. It had been built by
Beggar Boy, and was one of a number of such homes being
used by this energetic chipmunk. By the time we had
finished our digging, going cautiously so as not to cause
cave-ins and observing carefully each new section of the
tunnel exposed, we had followed a hole fourteen feet long.

Hi-Bub observed how the living quarters of Beggar
Boy were above the lowest level of the tunnel so that water
would drain properly. He looked with surprise and admiration on the cozy nest that had been made, all lined
with leaves, cedar bark and bits of cloth the little builder
had found somewhere. Then we came upon the granary
or food-storage room of the chipmunk. This was dug to
one side of the main runway and was elevated to ensure
drainage. The lowest point of the tunnel was three and
one-half feet below the surface. Hi-Bub had asked if
there was a back door, and presently in our digging we
came on his answer. The tunnel led from a main entrance
beside a large rock, down to the lowest point, then rose
again to emerge beneath a stump. This end of the long
hole was so wonderfully concealed it would never have
been discovered except by following the same course we
had. Hi-Bub giggled as he realized how intelligently his
little pet had planned this, so he could slyly slip out the
"back door" without being seen. Then he asked the question that always comes up in the thought of anyone investigating the ways of chipmunks.

"Sam Cammel," he said, hissing a perfect *S*. "Where's
all the dirt Beggar Boy dug out?"

"Yes, where is it, Hi-Bub?" I questioned. "If you know,

I wish you would tell me, for I don't know." We estimated that nearly a bushel of dirt had been removed in
digging that tunnel. Yet there was not an ounce of it to be
found anywhere around either "front door" or "back
door." It is one of the unsolved mysteries of nature. Of
course the chipmunk must carry this dirt away and dispose of it, probably with care that none of this freshly dug
earth be left to attract attention to his home. But in all my
years in the forest I have never seen a chipmunk do this,
and in fact I have never seen one dig a home. Furthermore, I have never met a nature student who has watched
this process. Someway even Hi-Bub's explanation that
"Little John Deer Foot helps them carry the dirt away"
didn't satisfy, though I enjoyed it. I hadn't heard much
about the 'maginary Indian boy lately and I missed him.

Giny, Hi-Bub and I searched through the book of nature, learning lines here and there, and yet feeling that in
this infinite volume we would never get beyond the first
chapter. We found Cheer's nest, with Mrs. Cheer sitting
devotedly over four eggs that were bluish-white with
black markings at the ends. Mrs. Cheer had selected a
home site in a swamp where bushes grew low over still
water. Here the nest would be quite safe from most creatures who prey on birds. Only the great blue heron or
perhaps the crow could reach it here, and Mrs. Cheer
knew well that her mate was capable of keeping such unwelcome guests away. Cheer proved this ability often.
Many times during the summer we saw him fearlessly at-
tacking such marauders, flying at them and pecking them

on the back of the head until they went crying and hurrying away.

We learned, too, some fragments of the language these redwings employ. During the all-absorbing responsibility of nesting days, Cheer became extremely alert. He came regularly to our feeding station, and was always his old friendly self. But he kept giving a new, shrill cry. We concluded that this was his way of remaining in communication with Mrs. Cheer. As long as there was no response from her, he felt free to stay on. But when a similar cry came from the nest, away he went at top speed to see what was wrong. On the occasions we heard this we found there was some danger present—such as a crow, raven or heron. Cheer promptly and bravely drove them away. We noted too that Cheer carried food to his mate while she was confined by nesting.

Cheer did a cute thing the day we located his nest. Giny, Hi-Bub and I were in the canoe. We knew the approximate area in which his nest would be because of Cheer's actions. Still it took quite a little searching. Mrs. Cheer flew from the nest as we drew near. She wasn't greatly frightened, however, and remained within fifteen feet of us. We looked closely at the nest, observing how wonderfully it was made, and how well selected was its location. Then we heard Cheer's voice. As we looked up we saw him winging toward us, crying as he came. Into the air directly over our heads he flew. There, to our amusement and amazement, he put on a demonstration of flying that was remarkable. It was simply aerial acrobatics. He glided, dipped and swerved. He fluttered his wings until he held himself in one spot in midair. He talked and sang. We called to him and applauded his performance. At first I believed he was trying to draw our attention away from the nest. However, I doubt that this was true. He showed not the least fear. Several times he dropped down to rest on the railing of the canoe. Hi-Bub interpreted the occasion best, I believe. "Tham Cammel," said he, so excited the lisp was back. "I gueth Cheer ith proud because he ith a daddy."

Hi-Bub had so many things to watch. Everything was at the hatching-out stage. There were three nests of robins on the island. Along the trail leading to Vanishing Lake we found the nest of the oven bird, built on the ground. Its shape suggested a Dutch oven. We located the nest of the white-throated sparrow, the red-eyed vireo and the whippoorwill.

Then we came upon one of those oddities of nature that keep students wondering just how such things begin. In a stump near the water's edge on the south shore of our island there was a song sparrow's nest. Hi-Bub found it. Whenever he was near such delicate things as birds' nests, he was so cautious you would have thought he was walking on the eggs themselves. There was something strange about this nest, and Hi-Bub nearly pulled one of my fingers off dragging me out to see it. In it we found three of the typical song sparrow eggs—bluish-white with brown specks. The thing that puzzled Hi-Bub was the fourth egg that was in the nest. It did not resemble the others in size or color. It was fully twice as large. Its color scheme was white, with numerous markings of chestnut and burnt umber.

"Ith that gonna be a big, big thong sparrow?" he asked, utterly bewildered by the problem before him.

"No, Hi-Bub," I said, "that's the egg of a cowbird."

"A cowbird?" he said, all ready to be amazed. "Does it give milk?"

I laughed. "A cowbird doesn't give milk, Hi-Bub," I explained. "It's seen around cows so often that name has been given it."

Then Hi-Bub learned about the strange habits of this common bird. The creature lays its eggs—from one to five—in the nests of other birds. Then it goes on about its social life, letting another mother bird hatch and rear its young. Usually when I find cowbird eggs in the nest of a smaller bird I remove them. I don't approve of this method of shifting parental responsibilities. Furthermore, the baby cowbird is so large he often pushes out the nest's legitimate children, and the foster mother unwittingly raises him at the loss of her own offspring. We decided we would leave this one alone, however, for Hi-Bub's education. In the days that followed this was the first place our lad visited when he came to the Sanctuary. The events of that nest fascinated him.

Hobo often held the center of the stage, however. The funny mongrel underwent a transition that amused and delighted us. We loved the homely, spirited little fellow and we wanted him around. His second visit occurred not too long after his tragic experience with the porcupine. We had decided to try him once more. Hi-Bub insisted he had talked with him and Hobo promised not to chase any animals ever again.

This promise was forgotten soon after he landed on the island. He was delighted to see us, and told us so by jumping up on us and licking our faces. He tried to say it in the usual doggy manner, though it was hard to wag that tail of his. It was so tightly curled over his back he could hardly move it. Hi-Bub said that when he did manage to wiggle his tail the end tickled his back. He knew this must be true because immediately Hobo sat down and began scratching. I fancied the itch was from other causes, but that opinion made no difference.

When greetings were finished, Hobo looked about in the usual cocky manner. I recognized the expression in his eyes and didn't like it. There was some repair work to do and I went into a shed to get some tools. When I came out I heard wild scrambling mingled with Hi-Bub's calls, "Hobo, come here! Here, Hobo!"

Hobo at the moment was intent on giving Beggar Boy some unsolicited exercise. Bushes and small trees were bending as the chase circled about the island. Suddenly Beggar Boy emerged from the brush near me, followed by the excited dog. Hobo was much closer to the chipmunk than I liked to see, and I jumped forward to delay him. The dog glanced up at me, and immediately a complete change came over him that left me at a loss for explanation. He ceased his running. The cocky look left his face. His tail lost much of its curl and tried to get between his legs. His head bent close to the ground and he let out a mournful howl.

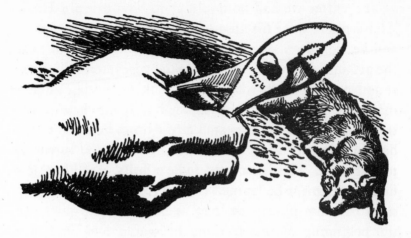

"What has happened?" I exclaimed in astonishment. Hobo lay flat on the ground and acted as if he would go lower if he knew how to do it. As I walked toward him, he cringed. "Hobo," I said, still puzzled, "I never treated you in any way that would make you so afraid of me. What's the matter?"

Hobo howled—the kind of cry that had been repeated so often during the porcupine adventure. Then I realized what was behind all this cowering. I held in my hand the very pair of pliers that had drawn out those quills. He wasn't afraid of me, but those pliers represented to him the greatest punishment he had ever known. Experimenting, I slipped the pincers into my pocket. Almost instantly Hobo's attitude changed. He rose from the ground and came to me. As I patted his head, he started looking for chipmunks or what have you. I drew out the pliers. Down he went to the ground and emitted a pitiful howl.

Thereafter we had no doubt as to how to train Hobo. Those pliers were his absolute master. One look at them and he would cease anything he was doing and crouch to the ground. We were careful not to overexercise this new-found power. Only when Hobo took to chasing an animal were they brought out. Immediately his chase would stop. When this was repeated a few times he came to understand that chasing something produced the threat of punishment. Then he ceased to be a bully. Within a few hours' treatment he learned he was free of the horrifying sight of those pincers so long as he remained quiet. In the beginning of this training he would look first at a chipmunk, then at the pliers. He would whine in his anxiety to make a charge. But it was as if those pliers had him by the tail, holding him back.

Within a few days there was a further transition in his attitude. The little fellow was really very sensitive to our wishes. In place of threatening him with the pliers, we began praising him for his self-restraint. When he did not chase a chipmunk or squirrel, he was a good dog and drew much petting and approval. He loved this attention. It wasn't many days before Hi-Bub was feeding Beggar Boy, Still-Mo and the others right before his nose. Hobo looked at the little creatures with an expression of delight on his face. He was completely won over. The animals of the island were no longer in danger from the dog. He had learned to love them, and in later days actually defended them when strange dogs came into the region.

Hi-Bub was immensely proud of his pet. "Hobo, you're a thwell dog," he said.

XVIII

WOODLAND BABES

Soon came that most interesting season when the forest is one great nursery. Baby animals were everywhere. We were busy day and night observing and making notes.

Under our cabin lived three infant woodchucks. Their story was unusual. When we first arrived, there had been four adult groundhogs. Then one of them, a little mother-to-be, announced that she had sole right to the island. The announcement came in the form of sudden belligerence against the others. She chased them about unceasingly. Strangely, they did not fight with her, but ran at her approach. This battle continued until three of the woodchucks departed from the island, leaving her in full possession. She then had a mighty fine home in which to rear the young. The babies had no fear of us and we had many a happy time with them.

Still-Mo, the red squirrel, had one young. It was a small family for her. The previous summer she had had three. She wasn't very proud or considerate of this youngster either. She cared for him until he was able to get about in that marvelous way squirrels have. Then she made him understand that he had to go forth into the world and seek his fortune. For several days she gave him no chance to rest. She chased him up and down trees, and round about

buildings—always talking in a way that I thought was
never used by a mother in speaking to her child. Finally
he left the island. We saw him swim to the mainland.
We found him there and fed him occasionally, but he
never returned.

Cheer was so busy gathering food that he almost ran
into himself coming and going from the feeding station.
His nest now had four youngsters in it—all with huge ap-
petites and even larger mouths. He had little time for us
during those days. There was nothing social about his
calls. Formerly he had paused as if he actually enjoyed
our society. Now even Hi-Bub could not coax him to stay
and visit. The moment the blackbird had his beak full of
food, away he went to try and appease the hunger that was
always calling him. Later, as soon as the young ones could
fly, he brought them to the feeding station. They were
awkward things, and had to beg bites from him and Mrs.
Cheer until gradually they learned to peck for themselves.
Cheer brought other adult males with him too—something that surprised us, for the nesting season was still prevailing. The first one of these we saw was a yearling, a
very beautiful bird which might have been from Cheer's
nest the previous season. We named him *Two Cheers*.
Then a second companion came with our pet. He was a
fully matured bird with very beautiful, glossy feathers—
quite equal in appearance to Cheer. We named him *Three
Cheers*.

We saw speckle-breasted baby robins following their
hard-working mothers around. There were fledgling song
sparrows and white-throated sparrows, with practically

no tails at all, always crying for food. There were young blue jays, of whom Blooey seemed very proud, who teased incessantly for parental attention.

At this time came an interesting adventure with the cowbird that had been reared by the song-sparrow mother. He was the only one that survived in her nest, and he filled it full. The noble little mother worked her feathers bare trying to feed him and satisfy his enormous appetite. At last he left the nest. I never saw a stranger or more pathetic sight in the bird world than this large fledgling (whom we named "the Brat") following his diminutive foster parent about, beak open, wings with a babylike flutter, begging for more and more of anything. The song sparrow stuffed and stuffed bugs and seeds into that haymow of a mouth, but the begging never ceased.

Then came an experience I am grateful to have had. Giny, Hi-Bub and I chanced to be at the right spot at the right time to witness it. The song sparrow and the Brat were going about their feeding routine when there appeared on the scene a female cowbird. The newcomer approached the other two and gave a peculiar little call. The Brat looked around, obviously confused. The song sparrow brought him another mouthful and he accepted it. However, he turned his attention to the adult cowbird. She gave him a bite of some food she had gathered. He accepted it. The song sparrow returned and made another contribution, then flew a short distance away, apparently expecting the Brat to follow. However, the cowbird persisted in her call and fed him again. When she flew away, he followed her, deserting his foster mother.

I had never seen this before. I have found no one else who has. Nevertheless, we saw this cowbird win back the affections of a youngster who had been farmed out to another species.

Many questions arise. Is this the usual method of making such youngsters, raised and educated by foster parents, realize to what species they belong? Was this the cowbird that had laid the egg in the song sparrow's nest? Then do cowbirds keep track of their young, ready to reclaim them at a chosen moment? It will take more observation than we have made to answer these questions. So far, all we know is that once at least a female cowbird coaxed a young one of her own species away from a song-sparrow mother who had raised it.

Back in the forest we heard new little voices in the coyote chorus. On the animal runways we found bear tracks—some so large my hand with fingers spread fitted within the margins, others as small as though Hi-Bub had stepped there barefooted. It wasn't difficult to imagine a tremendous old black mother bear trailing along with two or three awkward and cute young ones having their first lessons at living in the forest.

On one springtime hike we chanced on a polka dot of a fawn curled up in a hollow among some ferns. Hobo was not along with us that day and it was just as well, for I had enough trouble restraining Hi-Bub. He wanted to rush up and take the beautiful creature in his arms. I actually held him back while I explained something everyone who lives in these forests should know. Fawns such as this should not be touched or disturbed. At this age they are unable to walk for any great distance. The mother leaves them in hiding while she goes in search of food. Too often those who do not understand think such a fawn is lost or deserted. They take it in only to find that feeding a fawn successfully is a difficult thing to do. The mother, too, suffers when the young one is gone. "Just let him alone, Hi-Bub," I said to the struggling child. "His mother will come back as soon as we are gone. You wouldn't want her to find him missing, would you?"

No, Hi-Bub didn't want to injure anything that lives. But oh, how he did want that tiny creature in his arms!

This yearning was met in a better way rather soon. One evening we visited a salt lick which we maintain under close observation on the point of the mainland nearest our island. There we saw a beautiful doe licking at the cake of salt. She was most friendly in attitude. We wondered if this might be a deer we had known as Bobette, and successfully raised from babyhood. She had been liberated in this area at the end of her first year. Thereafter, although she was not tame, we believed she remembered us and came frequently to this place. The doe now standing before us permitted us to come within thirty feet of her. She showed nervousness when we attempted to go closer, so we stayed at this distance and talked to her. Hi-Bub was having the thrill of his life being so close to a deer. Then we discovered a fawn near at hand. It was a young creature, yet old enough to walk and run well. Presently the doe turned and went into the woods. We were surprised when the fawn did not follow. It kept nibbling at buds and leaves. As we looked at it more closely we noticed it was quite thin. Our next surprise was that it permitted us to approach. I held out my hand and it took my fingers in its mouth as if it were trying to nurse.

"Giny," I said, "I believe this little fellow is hungry. I wonder if we could feed him. See if you can keep him here until I get some milk."

I went to the island and returned as quickly as possible with a baby's bottle filled with warm milk. The fawn was still there. After much coaxing we got him to accept the nipple and he drank the entire bottleful. Another was brought over and he drank that too. Then he went into the brush in the direction the doe had taken.

The next night at about the same hour Giny and I returned to the salt lick. Hi-Bub was not with us that evening. The doe and fawn were there. The older animal soon retreated into the darkness, but the fawn stayed on. We prepared some more milk and the young creature nursed as before. Then it followed the doe into the woods. This became a nightly adventure.

So many of our conclusions about nature are mere guesses. My guess this time was that the old doe was the one we had known as Bobette. This was her fawn. For some reason the doe was not able to feed the fawn properly. Maybe with recollection of her own experience at our Sanctuary, she had brought the little one there. If this was her plan, it had worked perfectly. The fawn was eating fearlessly and well—while she, the mother, stayed close at hand to guard and guide the young one.

Hi-Bub named the new member of our Sanctuary staff "Specks" because of his speckled coat. Specks became the most important citizen of our woodland colony as far as we were concerned. Hi-Bub loved him. On the island our porcupine had been losing his caution and revealing that he was truly our old pet, Salt. He would permit us to pet him and would take his dinner from our hands. Yet our conversation was principally about Specks.

Most amazing was the friendship that sprang up between Hobo and the fawn. It was a case of love at first sight. The dog advanced cautiously to the fawn while I held the pair of pliers in my pocket ready for display in case disciplinary measures were necessary. There was nothing to fear. The fawn sniffed at the dog curiously. Hobo got more wag into his crooked tail than I had seen before. He stood on his hind legs and licked Specks in the face. He whined in his delight. Then he ran back to Hi-Bub and to me, pouncing up on us as if to call attention to

the lovely creature he had discovered. This was the beginning of a beautiful friendship in every sense of the
word. In those evenings when Hobo was at the Sanctuary, he knew the moment we began preparing a bottle
of milk where we were going. He was down by the boat
before we were, whining impatiently. Once on the mainland he went on a dead run in search of his fawn friend.
The old doe snorted at him on the first few visits, but soon
became reconciled to this strange companionship.

When, on several occasions, we took others who were
not often in our circle to see the fawn, Hobo showed a
definite distrust of the strangers. He placed himself between them and his fawn until he was sure of their inten-
tions.

"Sam Cammel," said Hi-Bub one evening after we had
visited Specks.

"Yes, Hi-Bub."

"Do you know why Specks came to us?"

"Why, no, Hi-Bub—I guess I don't for sure. Do you?"

"Yeth." A little lisp slipped in.

I waited for his explanation.

"Well—" he hesitated and looked at me as if making
sure his story would be taken at its true value—"well,
Little John Deer Foot brought him!"

"Did Little John do that?" I said seriously. "Oh, I am
so glad. He does such fine things."

"Yes," said Hi-Bub, pronouncing a good *s*. "He is
awful busy now. He takes care of all the baby animals."

While Hi-Bub's eyes grew heavy, I learned that the
Indian boy was working day and night "and other times

too," taking care of the little folk of the forest. He had
to keep them from falling into the water. He had to see
that they got enough to eat. He had to see that nothing
hurt them. When any of them were in trouble, it was
Little John Deer Foot who helped them out. So it was
when Specks's mother couldn't feed Specks any more.
"Little John Deer Foot took Thpecks by the ear," went on
the sleepy youngster, "an' brought him to Tham Cammel." It seems that our eyes were not sharp enough to see
it, but Little John Deer Foot was sitting on the cake of salt
when we fed Specks. "And Little John wuth—tho—tho
happy," said Hi-Bub as he bade the world good night.

XIX

GOOD MEDICINE FOR INDIAN JOHN

ONE DAY in early summer our trail again crossed that of Big John Shawano. In need of some supplies we couldn't get in our village, Giny and I drove to a larger town in a neighboring county. We learned from acquaintances there that Big John had been in town the day before on some banking business. The Indian was well known in this community. He had been born there. He and his father were on hand to welcome the first lumbermen and to help build the sawmill about which this town had grown.

It was fortunate for Big John that the businessmen were well acquainted with him, for his methods of doing business were far from orthodox. His conception of such dealings stemmed from his experience with nature. As has been said of gold, all things of the forest are where you find them. If Big John wanted berries, he went to berry patches and took them. If he wanted meat he took forest animals. If he wanted mushrooms he looked to the garden of the wildwood. Consequently, when he needed merchandise he went to the general store where such things were found—and, when he needed money, he went to the bank. Not that John ever asked something for nothing. He paid for what he got, always. But so far as he could see there was no difference in getting money from

184

a bank than in picking Juneberries from a neighboring knoll.

His need of money was not frequent, nor was it great. The trapping he did gave him an amount almost sufficient to purchase all store supplies. Occasionally his income was a bit short, however, or perhaps it did not come at the right time. This situation never bothered him, for just as he knew the animal runways of the forest, the berry patches and gardens of wild herbs, he knew where there were piles of money. There he went. It was a twenty-five-mile walk but he minded that not in the least.

One of our acquaintances had seen the tall Indian as he strode into the bank. The door shook on its hinges at the push he gave. He nodded a greeting to the bank president, who was his lifelong friend. Then he went directly to the teller's cage where he could see piles of money. As he approached the window, Big John took from under his jacket a most impressive-looking tomahawk. He paused for a moment to fondle it, for this was his most prized possession. The head of the weapon was made of steel, the handle carved of seasoned hickory. There were crude symbolic markings on the wood. Interested people and collectors had tried to draw from John the story of that tomahawk. They tried to buy both the story and the weapon. Neither was for sale. That revealed the strange and fascinating character of Big John Shawano. His sense of values was entirely apart from our rating of things. Certain possessions, both memories and objects, were his alone. He defended them against the world. He said that the tomahawk had been passed down to him from his father, who had received it from his grandfather. There the story ended, leaving listeners hungering for more. Like a hundred other tales rich in tradition and romance, this stayed in Big John's mental treasury—a realm where he lived in chiefly luxury and dignity. Here fancy mingled with memory, legend with history, fiction with fact, until John with fine disregard for any distinction between the real and unreal, built himself a world. This tomahawk belonged to that world, its value in the old Indian's eyes greater than a king's crown.

My friend said if he had not known Big John he would have had a severe fright as the Indian walked toward the cashier, tomahawk in hand. John held the weapon as if he meant to use it. His stride was powerful and purposeful, his face set and stern. However, the cashier anticipated no bank robbery. "Hello, John," he called cordially. "What can I do for you today?"

"Give me t'ree dollar!" commanded Big John, placing the tomahawk on the window ledge.

John's banking transactions would have startled Wall Street. Three dollars was the usual limit of the loan. Perhaps it was for flour, sugar, salt, underwear—whatever it was, it was certain to be the exact amount he needed.

The usual credit investigation and the signing of notes and papers were taboo in John's dealings. He got the money he requested without hesitation. As the smiling cashier passed the amount to him, John handed the tomahawk through the window. It was his security. The cashier took the weapon and reached to put it on a lower shelf.

"Here, you!" John spoke sharply. "You put him here!"
He indicated a place in plain view just inside the cage.
The tomahawk was put there—quickly.

"John pay—two moons," declared the Indian.

The cashier knew very well this promise would be kept.
In two months to the day that money would be repaid.
John would come through the bank door like a hurricane.
He would come to that window and lay three dollars on
the sill. Maybe it would be in nickels and pennies, but
every cent would be there. It had happened many times
before, and John never failed. There would be no interest paid on the loan, however. John couldn't see any sense
in paying for the use of money. The cashier knew also
that the tomahawk had better be in the exact spot where
the Indian had left it.

There was a disturbing strain in my friend's report.
Later in the day when he was driving home he had found
Big John Shawano sitting on a log at the roadside. It was
an unexpected sight to see the Indian resting. Our friend
stopped to see if all was well with him. John behaved
strangely, saying his "head go round" The man took him
into his car and drove him to the point where John's
trail leaves the highway. Here John refused further as-
sistance. He drew himself to his full height and threw his
packsack on his back and went down the trail. The man
watched him for a few moments. Noting that John walked
unsteadily the man called to ask if he should go along and
help him get home. "John all right," the fearless answer
came back. "He know what do."

Giny and I were quick to make our decision when we

heard this account of Big John. To think of him ill and alone in his solitary cabin greatly distressed us. We drove to his trail, parked our car and started afoot for his wilderness home. The trail showed little use. At some points it was rather hard to follow. Only John went over it and he did not often come out from his retreat.

The distance was said to be a mile and a half, but it seemed much longer to us. Perhaps anxiety had something to do with stretching it out. It is strange what pictures haunt the mind when there is concern and uncertainty. We had visions of John in a very bad way. We tried to thrust the suggestions out of our thoughts, but they were persistent.

We might well have spared ourselves all worry. Long before we reached the clearing at his cabin we heard the sound of wood-chopping. The strokes were frequent and powerful, and I knew no sick man was swinging that ax. As we looked out on the clearing we saw John make the last stroke to cut a large log in two. He put his ax to one side, then lifted a section of birch that would have defied a man of ordinary strength.

We remained concealed while we took in the frontier scene before us. John's log cabin was typical of the kind used by forest dwellers. It was small, about ten by fourteen feet, with one window and a door. Smoke was coming out the chimney. The cabin was well chinked. The grounds were reasonably neat and clean. At one side stood boards on which skins had been stretched to dry—part of John's winter trapping work. There was an outdoor fireplace made of loose stones where he did his summer cooking.

It was Big John himself who drew attention, however. He wielded both ax and saw in a masterly manner. He was about as far from being a sick man as a human being could be. We felt embarrassed at our presence there. It might be hard to make the Indian understand why we came. In a whisper Giny suggested we keep our visit a secret and return down the trail before he saw us. Then a huge black dog that looked more like a bear put an end to any such idea. He came from behind the cabin and, discovering us by either sight or scent, sprinkled unwelcoming barks all over the forest.

John sharply commanded the dog to silence while he looked around to discover the cause of this commotion. He picked up his ax and started in our direction. I felt grateful it wasn't a tomahawk, anyway. There was nothing to do now except to advance and declare ourselves, though I felt like a boy who has been caught stealing watermelons.

"Well, well—hello, John," I called as cordially as I could.

John looked at me challengingly. "What you want?" he asked gruffly. He stood motionless as he watched us advance toward him.

"Do you remember us?" I asked. I gave him our names and recalled places where we had met before, particularly the experience at Christmastime.

John did recall. His expression softened somewhat.

Then with an explosive "How!" he extended his hand to me. As a greeting for Giny there was just a large-sized grunt accompanied by a flutter of a smile.

"John," I said, "tell me—were you ill yesterday? If you were, how is it that you are so well today?"

John looked puzzled. "How you know?" he asked.

"We heard it through the man who drove you home. We were afraid you would need help, so we came to see you."

The old Indian's face was a study. Apparently this act of friendly interest touched him deeply. He had to struggle to retain his composure.

"You come far—ver' far—see if Big John well," he said, his eyes resting on me steadily.

"We knew you were alone, John," said Giny.

"Yes," said the old Indian in the nearest to a tender tone I had ever heard him use. "Yes, John lone. You care about John. You come see John. Good!" He turned his back to us and started for his cabin. We were not sure what we should do until he said, "Come!"

"Oh, we don't want to bother you, John," said Giny hastily. "You have work to do. You are all right, we can see that. We will go and let you work."

John looked about, once more the haughty chief. "Come!" he commanded in such sharp tones we were startled. Well, we went. We were discovering that when you are in John's company you do as he says.

We entered his cabin and he assigned us seats—consisting of wooden crates he had brought from town. The cabin was as clean as it could be with just a dirt floor. There was a small wood stove and above it hung his modest collection of cooking utensils. There was a cupboard in one corner in which were his dishes and some supplies. On the wall hung his rifle, his much-prized war club and articles of clothing. A pair of snowshoes stood in another corner. At one side of the small room was his bed, an amazing structure, the mere sight of which would literally be a pain in the neck to our comfort-loving generation. It was composed of two hardwood boards suspended between birch logs. There John slept winter and summer. Upon inquiry he told us he used blankets, just rolled up in them, put a piece of firewood under his head, "and sleep like rock!"

John was quite talkative now. We learned that he loved this "wigwam," as he called his cabin. People had wanted him to come and live in town, he said. They had offered him "big house." He would not go. He liked his little cabin out in the great forest. In winter, he said, it was best of all. His comments were hard to understand sometimes, but I gathered that he felt he was the only one in this forest world—"just God and John."

"Now, John," I said, feeling that we had reached the place where I could press my question. "You haven't told us what happened yesterday. Our friend was really concerned about you. Now what did you do?"

The tall Indian laughed loudly. "Much people make John sick," he said in a voice so deep it seemed to shake the walls of his cabin. "When John go town, men bump, men push, men hurry—John get mix up—get sick. John come home—take big medicine—no more sick."

"What medicine did you take, John?" asked Giny, deeply interested. "It worked a miracle."

"You not know?" he asked.

"No." Giny and I both felt guilty in our failure to understand.

Big John's face was a study. He looked at us incredulously for a moment, and then into his eyes came a faraway look that I had seen there before. It was as if he took a mental flight into a realm where we could not follow. He straightened up to his full height, raised his right hand above his head until his finger tips touched the roof of his cabin. Then he uttered a long, low chant in a strange tongue, probably the language of the Potawatomi. It was an odd experience for us.

"John," said Giny, in an effort to draw him back to conversation.

He continued his chant, seeming to have forgotten we were there.

"John, John!" Giny persisted. At length the old Indian looked down at her. "John, what *are* you saying? Can you tell us? We are so anxious to know."

I have never known whether he attempted an interpretation of his chant or if his English words expressed thoughts coined for our interest. "Wind blow, tall pine whisper—that good medicine," said our host slowly and impressively. "Eagle scream at dawn—good medicine. Great Spirit make big quiet—good medicine. Breath of forest, drink deep here—" and he beat on his huge chest with his fist—"good medicine. Woods God make—good medicine. Town man make—bah!"

He drifted into his native tongue again, carrying on a chant that ended in a mere whisper. Giny and I waited a long time, hoping he would tell us more about his big medicine. Our hopes were vain. The old Indian sat with his eyes closed, his lips now silent, his face turned upward as if in voiceless prayer. When he did speak again, it was with a startling change in subject and style.

"Where boy?" he asked.

"You mean Hi-Bub? Oh—he is back in the village with his parents," I replied.

"Good boy! Good boy!" Then John's eyes lighted up with interest and amusement. "He still talk spirit boy?" he asked.

"Spirit boy?"

"Yes, Indian spirit boy!"

I was puzzled for a moment, then realization came. John Shawano was remembering the imaginary playmate we had mentioned during our visit with him at Christmas. "You mean Little John Deer Foot, don't you, John?" I exclaimed. The Indian nodded, smiling. I explained that Hi-Bub still talked of his invisible companion.

The conversation dragged a little and not wishing to put a strain on our welcome, Giny and I rose to go.

"Sit down!" commanded John.

We sat down.

"You read!" demanded the Indian.

Without argument, I agreed to read.

John went to his crude cupboard. From a top shelf he

took a carefully wrapped package. Ceremoniously he un-
rolled the paper, until he held in his hand the very Bible
we had seen at Christmas.

"You read 'bout papoose come up," he said with chiefly
authority.

I hesitated, not knowing just what he meant.

"Papoose come up!" he thundered.

"I believe he means the Resurrection," interposed Giny.
It was a helpful suggestion and relieved a tense situation. I
found the account as given in Luke, and read it to the
Indian. He laughed deep and long, then requested that I
read it again. He asked that I read it a third time, then
a fourth. "Ho! Ho!" he laughed in loud triumph. "They
can't kill that one. He come up. He know big medicine.
He tell how!"

By gestures and broken English he told us that some
day he would "come up" as Jesus had. He would go to
his people, who he said lived beyond the setting sun. He
would teach them what the Big Book said, and "everybody come up."

The conversation was interesting, but at last Giny was
able to make our determined host understand that we must
reach home before dark.

"Ugh," he grunted, "you go!"

As we were leaving the door Big John took his war club
from the wall. "You like?" he asked, extending the ancient
weapon to me.

"Yes, John, I like that very much," I replied.

"You take!" he commanded, offering the gift to me.
Then with an unexpected outburst of humor he added,

"You take—no use on squaw," pointing to Giny. We all laughed.

"But John, this is valuable," I protested. "You should not give it away. Let me buy it from you."

"John *give*," he snapped with finality. "You come see John. You friend. John like much."

He had trouble with his words, but there was no question that Big John Shawano was grateful for our interest in him and for our friendly visit. I accepted the war club with the realization that John was giving me one of his most prized possessions.

"We had a precious experience with that grand old character," said Giny as we were driving home.

"It will make a wonderful memory," said I.

"Indeed it will," she agreed. "A memory that will be a constant challenge to make our faith pure, strong and yet simple."

XX

COONLETS

THE summer was unusually rich in colorful sunsets and still evenings. Nature, enforcing her ironclad rule that no two things shall be alike, keeps her years and seasons new and original. Each one has its individual charm. As a rule sunsets of awe-inspiring splendor are not frequent. There is beauty to the close of every day, yet the brilliant effects that really make a visible symphony of the heavens are rare. That is why we were surprised when evening after evening such glory ruled the sky that we were drawn from other interests to watch it.

The still evenings led to many campfire gatherings. These are beneficial experiences. There is something profoundly virtuous about being wholly quiet. The grandest sermons, the real revelations of understanding, never come by way of speaking and hearing. They are whispered deep within our hearts and the disquieted mind does not hear them. It takes deep silence of thought to learn these truths "written in the fleshly tablets of the heart."

Conversations are important and helpful when they verify what we already know. Hence around our campfires there must be friends. Ada, Ray and June often came in their canoe. Frequently Hi-Bub and his parents were there too. They were now living in a summer cabin on an

196

adjacent lake, and would row over to join us. Neighbors dropped in. Sometimes our circle included twenty or more. Always there was singing, to the accompaniment of my guitar. If you want to see forest life at its best, drift in a canoe at some distance from such a group. Look back at the magic of the flames as they light up the trunks of the trees and outline the smile that comes so naturally to every face. Hear the grand quality that wholesome joy puts into all voices. In this scene of scenes is harmony beyond mere tones—it is poetry incarnate.

We wondered at Salt during these campfire assemblies. Obviously he liked them. No such evening had progressed very far until we would see him moving slowly and silently into the outer fringe of the firelight. There he would lie in that funny manner of his, flat on his tummy, front legs beside his nose, hind legs stretched out beside his tail, foot soles turned upward. He responded little to those who petted him and he never uttered a sound. This latter fact puzzled us. As near as we knew he had not made a call all summer. It was strange, since he was such a talkative creature in previous years. Salt was a valuable addition to the party, however.

Two other members came from the wilds. A pair of loons often floated up within fifty yards of the island and joined in on some of our choicest barber-shop harmonies with their cries. In truth they were at times so persistent in their own original melodies that they made it difficult for us to follow our tunes or stay in pitch. Always we laughed at them and they laughed right back.

With our little friend Specks, the passing weeks

brought less and less intimacy. He was our close companion through the bottle stage only. As he had less and
less need of our food he became more aloof. He would
play with Hobo, though, and it was amusing to see. They
would race about the brush, sometimes dog chasing fawn,
sometimes the reverse. Specks seemed to delight in doing
things that made Hobo's going difficult. He would jump
gracefully over logs or brush piles and then look around
to see the short-legged dog scrambling awkwardly over
the barrier or running far around. Sometimes Hobo
growled and barked as if he meant to bite the spots off his
playmate. Occasionally Specks struck out with his front
feet savagely in Hobo's general direction. From back in
the woods we heard the whistling snort of the old mother
doe, as though she disapproved of such roughness. Yet
always the play ended with dog and fawn each licking the
other's face. Hobo would come running up to Hi-Bub's
waiting arms with many a glance backward as if saying,
"Hot dog, I had a good time." Specks would look around,
too, with the same message in his beautiful eyes.

For ten days in midsummer raccoons ceased to come to
our feeding station. We understood this period of inter-
mission. Each year it had occurred. Back in the forest in
hollow trees were the homes of the ring-tailed coons. During spring and early summer these homes house the little
ones. They have long babyhoods compared to most other
animals. They are left at home with definite orders to stay
there while the parents roam about feeding. Then comes
time for the young to leave the nest and learn how to be
raccoons. At first their journeys are short. Certainly they

are not then ready for the cold and hazardous swim to our island. So at this stage of their development the parent animals do not try them with tasks beyond their strength. The young are following the older ones, and if the grown-ups swam out into the lake the children would attempt it. Hence there are no journeys to our island until the coon-lets are equal to it.

We do not stop putting food out during this temporary absence. It is impossible to know just when their visits will be resumed.

One night we heard the cute trilling cries we had been expecting. We were glad it happened during an evening when Hi-Bub was with us. We turned our flashlights on the feeding pan. Out of the night, silent as the darkness itself, came Racket. Cautiously she peered about. Then she snatched a piece of bread and disappeared into the near-by brush. We knew what was going on. Back in there were the young. She was introducing them to a new kind of food. Several times she came forward for an additional sample. She did not act like the Racket we had known for two years, who was so very friendly. Now she had the responsibility of motherhood. Her young must be taught to be careful. Her example was their instruction.

For an hour Racket worked at carrying bites to her con-cealed family. Then we heard new movement in the brush and leaves. Presently the beam of our flashlight rested upon three bright-eyed baby faces peering at us from close to the ground. We wanted to scream with delight. Racket came forward, showing them a proper attitude of caution, to which they now paid little attention. The pan of food

simply fascinated them, and they pitched in with unrestrained enthusiasm. We shook with suppressed laughter at the way they felt about with their front feet, selecting with an acute sense of touch the morsels they preferred.

"Aren't they cute, Hi-Bub?" whispered Giny. "They
look like three little gray muffs."

"Uh-huh," answered Hi-Bub, his whisper having a
little solid voice in it. "Do you know their names, Mithuth
Cammel?"

"Why, no. Do they have names already?"

"Uh-huh."

I presumed Little John Deer Foot had had something
to do with the christening, but not wanting to get into any
elaborate explanation at that time, I simply asked, "What
are their names? They will have to be good ones for three
such cute coons."

"Amos, Andy and the Kingfish," said Hi-Bub with assurance.

Giny and I wanted to break out into a big laugh, but we restrained ourselves. "Fair enough, Hi-Bub, fair enough!" I exclaimed in low voice. "Amos, Andy and the Kingfish they shall be."

Amos, Andy and the Kingfish took to our island as their mother had. Within a few days we found they were not leaving the island at all but were living under the cabin. The mother came and went, but not they. Once in her baby days when she was ill she had come to live on the island. Perhaps then she had felt the safety of the place and now she sought that same sanctuary for her cubs.

Whatever inspired the move, we were glad to have them. Those three little woolly creatures were a constant delight to us. They became more and more confident of our friendship. At times they came out in full daylight— an unusual thing for the raccoon who for generations has preferred the cover of darkness for his wanderings.

Late summer saw some definite developments in the life of Old Charley, the bear. Our attempt to draw him and hold him at our feeding station in the woods had been a flat failure. He liked the food we put out all right, but getting it wasn't exciting enough. Seldom did we see him and generally our servings were consumed by jays, crows, squirrels, chipmunks and mice.

Old Charley's disposition was not improving to any degree. With more people coming into the region for vacations, he found new ways to get in trouble. One stunt of his was to lie down in the middle of a road and force a car to stop. He would not move an inch until bits of food were tossed out the window for him. The stretch of highway where he did this was sometimes referred to as "Old Charley's Toll Road."

He loved picnics, and he was a greater handicap to them than all the sand, ants and mosquitoes combined. Once he stole a lunch basket, picked it up in his mouth by the handle and ran into the woods. It was never found again. Another time a dozen picnickers left their food on a table while they went for a short hike. When they returned, Old Charley sat in the middle of the table having the time of his life. They beat on pans, yelled and danced around. As far as Charley was concerned this was just a good floor show. He didn't leave until he had eaten everything, or else mauled it so no one else wanted to eat it. Then he jumped down and ran away, completing the devastation by kicking the table over as he went.

At last he met his match. A trapper was brought into the region who knew a great deal about handling such animals. A large box was built of strong material. A door was arranged at one end so it would spring shut when anything entered the box. Inside was placed a large piece of bacon tied to a string that released the trap door. Old Charley couldn't resist the smell of that bacon. The trap had been set for him only a few nights when he entered it. The next morning the trapper found his prize sound asleep inside the box. Charley accepted his captivity philosophically. He grinned at the men as they laboriously loaded him on a truck. Away went Old Charley as he had come, with a special escort and a specially prepared conveyance.

Old Charley was taken to a zoo in a large city. Months later I stopped to see him. There he was in a good barless cage with several other bears. He did not know me, of course.

"Ever have any trouble with the bears?" I asked casually of the keeper who was working near at hand.

"No—they're good animals, easy to handle," said the man. Then he straightened up and looked at me. "That is, all of them are O.K. except that fellow with one ear. He's a devil. He steals my broom, my hat, my pipe, and bites the garden hose until it leaks. He's a devil, I tell you. There, now—look at that grin on his face!"

Old Charley was wearing his typical expression. Blinking his eyes he looked about as if to say, "O.K.—I don't care where I am. Just as long as there are people to pester it's all right with me."

XXI

BOYS' WEEK

THE WEEK toward the close of August in which little
Tony and Hi-Bub stayed at the Sanctuary will always remain one of the most prized memories of our forest home.

Tony came by train. He had been fathered and moth-
ered by the entire crew and the passengers. No one could
look at him without wanting to do something for the
youngster. He had made great gains since we saw him in
the winter. Undoubtedly he was rising above the illness
that had assailed him and he was bound for strong manhood. Still there was a look of frailty in his thin face, and
his prevailing mood was one of such quiet meekness that
all who saw him wanted to pour joy, confidence and living
interest into his thoughts.

Tony needed the Sanctuary. Hi-Bub needed it too but
in a different way. With Hi-Bub it was sort of a spiritual
gymnasium where he could exercise the dynamic qualities
latent in his character. Tony was in much the same position as the young forest creatures that came where they
could have protection until their strength was equal to
the demands of life. His thought was as frail and sensitive
as his body appeared. I compared him to the tender shoot
of a young red pine that had worked its way through the
crust of the earth to look at sunlight, drink of dew, hear

bird songs. They look so delicate that even the buffeting of the evening breeze might be too severe. Yet they have within them a strength not seen by human eye or recognized by human mind. In secret ways they draw from the world the nourishment, the protection, the love vital to their growth. One day they will rise to their lofty position in forest life, pillars of strength, their roots helping to hold the very earth together.

"Tony is a good boy," said a letter he brought from his mother, in which she told of certain special care he would need. "He is so different from other children it has made him lonely in the world. Perhaps that was the beginning of his present problem. He needs sympathy and understanding. He thinks in terms of poetry. The hardness found in the world hurts him severely. He wants to live in dreams. Some members of our family try to shame him or shock him out of this but I do not. His dreams are good dreams and I want him to have them. I know the quiet of your Sanctuary will give him an opportunity for this."

"Yes, Tony," I said to myself as I read this. "You may dream here to your heart's content. No one will try to awaken you, for we are dreamers too, in a way. Out of what are called dreams has come much of the goodness known in the world. Good dreams are closer to reality than the illusions that spring from fears and selfishness."

There was a dignity about Tony that was baffling. We never once got so close to him as we did to Hi-Bub. There was always the feeling that, like Big John Shawano, Tony looked out at us from another world. I told him to call me Sam for convenience. He couldn't do it. I was "Mr.

Sam Campbell (pronounced plainly Camp-bell) and nothing else would do. Giny was "Mrs. Camp-bell," though our young visitor was invited to call her Giny, or Aunty.

I had wondered if I would get much work done during this week. Publishers were pressing me for manuscripts and I needed many hours at my desk. There was no reason to be concerned. Hi-Bub took over completely the task of entertaining and instructing his friend. When they were snugly settled in their little cabin home, Hi-Bub put his arm around Tony. It wouldn't go far around, but he made it go as far as he could. Tony responded the same way. There isn't anything much more awkward than youngsters that age endeavoring to embrace each other. Tony nearly fell down with Hi-Bub's impact, and when he threw his arm around Hi-Bub's shoulders, it looked like a juvenile wrestling match. It was perfectly satisfactory to them, however, and expressed the love they wanted it to. Then out they went to search for adventure.

Tony had to meet the island pets one after another, with Hi-Bub presiding as host. "Thith ith Th-tubby," he said as the veteran chipmunk came up to them. Excitement was bringing out the lisp.

"Who?"

"Th-tubby!"

"Oh," said Tony, who was familiar with the names of these animals through my books. "You mean Stubby."

"I thaid Th-tubby."

"Stubby!"

"Th-tubby!"

I don't know where this clash of phonetics would have led if Cheer had not flown up at that moment. Tony's expression was something to study as he recognized the bird. Here in real life was the creature that had become a symbol of happiness to him. His mouth fell open and his sensitive eyes grew wide with wonder.

Cheer played his part beautifully. He lighted on a branch of a tree about five feet from the two boys. There he sang his limited but lovely repertoire of songs. He strutted back and forth, spreading his wings so as to display to full advantage the gorgeous red spots. Hi-Bub giggled in unrestrained glee. Tony laughed too, but it seemed a little hard for his giggles to get out.

"Lookut! Lookut!" cried Hi-Bub, grabbing Tony's head and trying to force his attention toward Cheer.

"I am lookuting," said the soft voice of Tony.

They fed Cheer. The bird was bewildered and half frightened at the insistent way it was done. Each boy held out a handful of peanut crumbs, and each wanted the bird as his exclusive customer. They poked their small hands out toward Cheer so violently he wasn't sure they were not striking at him. In the meantime Stubby was around demanding attention. Beggar Boy raced up for an introduction and some peanuts. Still-Mo the red squirrel joined the party. Blooey the blue jay cried for service. Hi-Bub dragged Tony from one exciting adventure to another until the young visitor had to sit down on our doorstep. He was not permitted to rest long, however, for Hi-

Bub had discovered Salt the porcupine asleep high in a pine tree. Tony stood with his head back watching the porky so long he had difficulty straightening up again.

Really Hi-Bub's tender consideration for his little pal was heart-touching. Presently Giny suggested that Tony might be tired and need some rest. They took him to the little cabin and tucked him in bed. Hi-Bub did the tucking. He did it so thoroughly Giny had to loosen the covers for fear Tony would be unable to breathe. Hi-Bub kept asking him if he was all right until Tony closed his eyes to get rid of him.

While Tony had his first nap, Hi-Bub came to my desk. "Don't you think you ought to have a nap too, old top?" I asked. Hi-Bub just shook his head. He leaned against me and I put my arm around him. "Having fun?" I asked. He nodded again. He had something to say and I knew it, but he was having a hard time getting it to come out.

"Sam Cammel," he said softly.

"Yes, Hi-Bub?"

"Do you s'pose . . ." He hesitated and shot a glance up at me.

"Suppose what, old top?" I asked.

"Well—do you s'pose Little John Deer Foot would care if I didn't have him any more?"

"Why, Hi-Bub?" I asked, wondering what was coming.

" 'Cause I just want Tony," he said earnestly. "Tony is solid, kind of. I like Little John too, but . . ." The sentence ended in a sniff.

"Why, I'm sure Little John Deer Foot wouldn't mind,"

I said reassuringly. "He wants everyone to be happy. He wants you to do everything you can to help Tony. Little John has lots to do."

"Yeth," agreed Hi-Bub, the lisp working again. "You thee, he hath all the animalth and flowerth and woodth."

"Sure," I said in my strongest tone of conviction. "You go on and have just Tony. Little John Deer Foot won't care at all."

Away Hi-Bub went, happy as Cheer himself. He played with the animals, talking to them constantly. His voice was louder than usual. I noticed too that he managed to get right under Tony's window. Altogether his efforts greatly shortened Tony's nap.

No one ever had a more thorough course in nature in one week's time than did Tony. Hi-Bub led him around continually. He told him things about nature that would have astonished an experienced naturalist. Yet there was a lot of good teaching done. I always have believed that children can teach children far better than any adult can. Hi-Bub confirmed my conviction. Within two days Tony could identify most of the common trees about us. He knew the track of a deer and a bear. He could point out the wild aster, the bunchberry, white water lily, cotton grass and other plants of the season. Hi-Bub had him walking around on tiptoe, stepping in spots where there were no leaves or twigs. That was the way Indians went through the woods. He made him whisper much of the time so as not to disturb the forest.

We had been told that Tony couldn't eat or sleep very well. If we had not been informed, we would never have learned it from observation. The first night he was so tired and so filled with fresh air he was in bed before dark, and asleep as soon as his head touched the pillow. This delighted Hi-Bub. "Oh boy," he said the next morning, "he thnores! He make-th a thound like a bullfrog."

At the table Tony was the last to finish eating. "What do you do with it?" asked Hi-Bub, quite seriously. "You haven't any tummy."

Tony just smiled and passed his plate for more. Giny had obtained a list of Tony's favorite foods, and she saw to it that he had an abundance of them.

There was an interruption to Tony's first dinner, how-ever—all prearranged. Hi-Bub had helped plan it. Tony had not been told what was going to happen, but he knew very well something was in the offing, for Hi-Bub simply could not keep his giggles and wise looks controlled.

It was evening when we sat down to the table. The door had purposely been left slightly ajar. Our meal was about half finished when suddenly Hi-Bub's giggling became in-tensified. He glanced toward the door. Tony looked in that direction, and what he saw put him in a state of sus-pended animation, with a large bite of something or other only partly chewed. There, peering at us in their cute questioning style, were Amos, Andy and the Kingfish. Three prettier raccoons never walked the forest floor. Their coats were now heavy and silky. The black line across their eyes was so well defined it looked as if it had been painted. Their eyes were like shining beads, their cupped ears alertly forward, their tails bushy and ringed with dark streaks. Looking up at us they seemed to be asking, "Is it all right, may we come in?"

They had been in many times before, always wisely choosing the dinner hour. We had kept this habit a secret from Tony, as a surprise for him. The plan was oversuccessful. He not only stopped eating, he nearly stopped breathing. He shot quick glances at Giny, Hi-Bub and me to see if we all saw the same thing. Hi-Bub probably answered the question in his thoughts. "Yeth, Tony, it'th real. Really it'th real!"

Tony answered with a brief lightning flash of a smile, then resumed his expression of wonderment. Not a word did he say nor sound did he make for fully three minutes. He just watched the three coons as they cautiously came farther into the room and finally right to the table.

"Tony," I said, "if you want to, you may give them bites of food from your plate. They will take it from your fingers. Don't be afraid."

I demonstrated for his benefit how the little creatures would rise on their hind legs and reach high to get a choice nibble. Then Tony tried it. There was some timidity when Amos came right up to him. He drew his hand back slightly. The coon reached out quickly with his front feet and caught the morsel Tony held. Then Tony laughed loud and hard. The three visitors went scurrying out the door at the sound. They were back again within a minute, however, and the show went on.

Tony fed them everything on his plate. He gave them everything on Hi-Bub's plate too. I think he would have served them everything on the table had we not called a halt. Believing that we also had some need of nourishment, I led the three coons out the door under enticement of a handful of peanuts—their favorite food.

Every night this act was repeated. Tony never ceased to marvel at the spectacle of these forest creatures coming right into the house. Great things will happen in that boy's life, I am sure. There are talents within his make-up that will carry him far. However, I doubt if life will ever offer him a greater thrill than when he saw Amos, Andy and the Kingfish—three young coons—walk into his dining room.

So this wonderful week slipped by. Every hour we felt grateful that we were privileged to peek into the world of childhood this way. Hi-Bub never ran down. He had ideas continually that kept them on the go. Twice we sacrificed a little sleep to see Specks and his mother. Tony could hardly believe what he saw. Deer had always lived only in storybooks or pictures for him. Now to see one almost within reach was a glorious experience. There were no cute sayings from Tony, such as were constantly spouting out of Hi-Bub. To learn his reactions we had to study closely the expressions in his eyes and on his face.

I had feared there would be tears when it was time for Tony to go home. That shows I didn't know Tony. He climbed on the train without one expression of regret. He thanked us plainly, as he had been told to do by his mother. We asked the train crew to look after him. It was a waste of words to do so. Tony had hardly reached his seat when he was the center of attention. Everyone wanted to do something for him.

Giny, Hi-Bub and I watched the train pull out. Our own hearts were under a strain.

"Sam Cammel," said Hi-Bub.

"Yes."

"Tony is a thwell guy."

Later we had a letter of gratitude from Tony's mother. "He is so quiet, I wonder if you understand what a wonderful time he had and what an inspiration this trip was to him. I think you would like to have these verses I found among his school papers. They show what an impression was made on his thoughts."

Here are the little verses Tony wrote:

> Sometime I would like to know
> What makes such lovely things grow.
>
> I want to know and I'm sure I will
> What makes the woods so very still.
>
> I'd like to know just one more thing
> What causes little birds to sing.

XXII

SQUIRRELY WISDOM

SEPTEMBER is a sort of hilltop in the year. From its crest you can look back on the lush green valleys of spring and summer. In the other direction lie the long, colorful slopes of autumn. At the horizon is the white loveliness of winter. In itself September is a mixture of what has been and what is coming. Its days borrow something from August, its evenings have frost on their breath.

This begins fireplace season. Giny and I like to use this period of coziness to take inventory of our experiences and blessings. It is good for anyone to do this occasionally. It brings a realization of the goodness that is forever flowing into life. There is another benefit. It utterly defeats the notion that time is some flapping and fluttering independent thing that just delights in breaking all speed records. "Time flies," and "where does the time go?" indicate an error in our own thinking rather than some property residing in clocks and hour glasses. By the time we had reviewed the events of the season, dwelt on the lessons we had learned and expressed a measure of gratitude for it all, we could only say in honesty, "What a long, lovely, blessing-packed summer this has been."

There were changes at the Sanctuary this September. Hi-Bub was in school and could visit us only on week ends as he had done the previous year. Cheer had departed. The general migration of redwings was in late August. As in the previous autumn, Cheer lingered on to give us something extra of his companionship, but his date of departure was earlier by several weeks than in the first year of our acquaintance. We missed him terribly. Hi-Bub called for him until the woods echoed. "It is no use, Hi-Bub," I said to the lad. "Cheer is gone."

"Where did he go?" he asked.

"Oh, 'way down south where the palm trees grow," I replied. "Maybe he is in Georgia, Mississippi or Florida."

Hi-Bub was thoughtful for a moment. "Do you s'pose he went to make someone happy as he did Tony?" Hi-Bub wanted a good reason back of everything.

"Yes, old top," I assured him. "Everyone who looks at Cheer and understands him will be happier—wherever he goes."

"He'th a thwell bird," murmured Hi-Bub.

Specks was becoming wilder and more spirited. His coat was thickening, though the baby spots still showed plainly. Amos, Andy and the Kingfish, together with Racket their mother, were preparing for winter. Their fur was growing heavy and even more beautiful.

September brought one unhappy event to our north country. It was the season for bow-and-arrow hunting. Sportsmen who like the Robin Hood type of weapon were wandering the woodlands outside our Sanctuary. It wasn't pleasant to think of the scenes they might create among the forest creatures. My only consolation was that they are usually such poor marksmen that few of their arrows do any damage.

Still-Mo the red squirrel now startled us by bringing to view a family of six young ones. This was her second brood of the year, as she had brought forth one baby in July. The first definite news we had of the new family was when we heard many tiny feet scampering about our attic. Soon after that we saw them briefly sunning themselves on the roof of the kitchen. I refused to attempt naming them. Still-Mo had given us such a problem in titling her children anyway. "Let's wait until spring," I said to Giny. "Perhaps some of them will have left the island by that time and won't need to be named."

Still-Mo gave us lots to think about in her handling of this belated family. She left us with many unanswered questions too.

Most nature students feel sure that animals are not good weather prophets. Like our own weather men, they make mistakes. Yet there is evidence that sometimes at least they instinctively know what is going to happen. Here is how Still-Mo proved this fact to us. One Saturday when Hi-Bub was at the Sanctuary, I heard him calling loudly from back of the cabin, "Sam Cammel, Sam Cammel— come quick!"

I hurried out, not knowing whether he had climbed a tree and forgotten the way down, if he were attacked by a *hodag*—or what was happening. He was standing looking up at our roof. "Still-Mo is eating her babies," cried the excited boy. "Come quick!"

I reached his side and looked up to see Still-Mo emerging from her entrance to our attic. It was easy to see where Hi-Bub got his notion of what was happening. Still-Mo was carrying one of her young. Now the red squirrel totes her papoose in a very odd manner. She bites right into the stomach of the youngster, whereupon the little one wraps himself around her head to hang on—perhaps more through pain than love. It is a mighty firm grip they have on each other, and probably this is the only way the mother could carry her fuzzy little offspring and retain freedom to travel up and down trees. I quieted Hi-Bub's fears about Still-Mo making a meal of her babies. We called Giny and the three of us watched carefully what was going on.

Still-Mo was moving. One at a time she carried her little ones out of the attic, down a tree to the ground, across about fifty feet to a maple tree and up into its top branches. There she placed her brood in a hollow that had been prepared for them. It took about thirty minutes to complete the transfer. Then the busy mother ran away on some other tasks.

Presently the youngsters came boiling out of their living "log cabin." It was the first tree they had seen and they loved it. They began exploring every branch, twig and leaf of that maple. There was no need to worry about them. This tree-climbing business was in their blood and they were born expert at it.

The thing that interested us most about this event was how it fitted into a weather pattern. We had been having a spell of autumn cold and rain. During this period the squirrel family stayed snugly tucked in the attic. When we saw Still-Mo engineering the transfer of her youngsters, the first break was showing in the storm clouds. The skies cleared very soon thereafter and the little chickarees had sunshine to play in and a mellow breeze to warm them. For three days they lived in the maple tree, getting acquainted with their sylvan world. Sometimes Still-Mo led them in routes through the branches, sometimes they carried out their exercise alone.

On the fourth day there was excitement again among the squirrels. Still-Mo was taking them on a new adventure. She led two of them across the ground to a tree that stands beside our house. From this tree Still-Mo generally jumps to the roof on her way to the attic nest. It is quite a jump, but apparently she prefers this route over that leading through other trees where the ascent is easier.

As we watched her, we realized she was schooling her little ones in this jumping maneuver. They followed her

closely and did their best. She led them up the difficult
path and made the jump as an example to follow. The
young hesitated. Still-Mo jumped to the tree again and
nuzzled them as if saying, "Come on there, little ones.
Are you going to let the older generation show you up?"
Again she leaped through space to the roof.

One youngster followed successfully and chattered as
if quite proud of his accomplishment. The other one
couldn't work up the courage to try. He ran to the end of
the limb, looked over to the roof, and then retreated to a
crotch and sat there trembling. Still-Mo jumped back to
him. She poked him with her nose to urge the attempt.
It was no use. He was just plain afraid. When Still-Mo
had determined this, she deliberately led him down that
tree and over to another much closer to the roof. Two at
a time the rest of the family were put through this training. Of the six little ones, four made the big jump successfully, two had to be taken over the easy path. Still-Mo
worked without rest until they were all in the attic again.

Then came the weather angle. Within two hours after
this family had returned to its well-insulated quarters, a
terrific storm broke. In the hollow tree the nest would
have been flooded. The baby squirrels might not have
survived. One can always charge such things to chance
and coincidence if he wishes. There could be no final
proof of wisdom or foresight on the part of Still-Mo unless we could actually read her thoughts. The fact re-
mains that she took her family out for tree training exactly
at the time weather suitable for such experience was be-

ginning. She brought them in precisely when this period of good weather was over and a storm that could have done serious damage to her family was at hand.

There is another observation that must be added to this history of Still-Mo. In an earlier chapter I told how Still-Mo's single July baby was soon driven off the island. It was early in the season and he had plenty of time to find another home for himself and store up his winter food. How different was the treatment of the six that we saw in September! Now winter was close at hand. There was no time to look for homes and certainly not sufficient opportunity to gather enough seeds, nuts and pine cones. We noticed prior to the coming of the second family that Still-Mo had worked hard at putting food in the attic. There must have been a tremendous store on hand. Soon we understood the purpose. After the young squirrels had been given sufficient training so that they could take care of themselves, Still-Mo deliberately abandoned the attic to them and went to live elsewhere on the island! There the little fellows had a grand store of provisions willed to them, and a place that would be safe and comfortable during the cold period just ahead.

I believe the intelligence and purpose of this act cannot be questioned. Still-Mo realized all the conditions facing this September family. She prepared for her young in a motherly and wise way. The sentiment of conscious sacrifice was there. Such displays of character on the human scale are called noble, and we can say no less of these acts of that interesting and lovable little chickaree, Still-Mo.

XXIII

UNHAPPY HUNTING GROUND

Hi-Bub's daddy went away on a short business trip. Such journeys occurred at intervals, and they were a matter of much interest to Hi-Bub. Not that he knew anything about the business involved. As far as he was concerned that was just an incident. The important thing was that when Daddy returned, with him would come a thoughtful present for Hi-Bub.

When the fond daddy returned from his autumn journey, Hi-Bub was in possession of a gift that concerned me almost as much as it did him. It was a shiny new box camera! I was closely connected with the deal. I had recommended that Hi-Bub be introduced to photography to broaden his interest in nature. Furthermore, I had promised to teach him the use of the camera and to help him learn the art of camera hunting.

It is my conviction that the camera habit is good medicine for the mind. All that is learned from this fine hobby is constructive. Beauty, as everyone knows, is not something that resides in nature. Beauty is a quality of human thought. The more we cultivate this quality by seeking the world's loveliness, the more beauty we find. Just as a muscle is strengthened with use, so this precious talent is developed by exercise. A camera demands that you diligently seek the better views of nature and life. It keeps you thinking in terms of beauty.

In nature the camera has another outstanding virtue. It leads its user to think in terms of life. The camera hunter does not want to destroy and disturb the creatures of forest and field. An animal or a plant is a good subject only so long as it is alive and interesting.

For these reasons I wanted my friend Hi-Bub to begin a career as a photographer. The camera he had would never have excited the envy of Hollywood camera men. It had a fixed focus and its lens was only a little stronger than a window glass. But it would take pictures, and that was enough for Hi-Bub. I remember so well the way he looked when his daddy brought him to the island. The boy could hardly wait for the boat to reach the shore. He came bounding out, his little overnight bag in one hand and this precious new possession in the other, crying, "Tham Cammel, Tham Cammel!"

"What in the world is it, Hi-Bub?" I asked.

"It'th a camera, it'th a camera, it ith, it ith," he sputtered. "All you do ith preth this thingamajig and it take-th pictures!"

Giny came running down to see the new contraption. Hi-Bub showed us how to use the view finder, and then thought the camera was broken when his own hand got in the way of the finder and shut off the image.

"I see where we have a job on hand, old top," I said, delighted at the prospect. "No doubt you'll find there is more to taking pictures than just pressing down on that thingamajig. What do you say—shall we start out to make an entire album of our animal friends?"

Nothing could please Hi-Bub more. The task was more difficult than he supposed, however. Picturing animals is not easy, not even friendly ones such as dwell on our island. They aren't interested in photography, and have a rare faculty for doing just what they shouldn't do from the camera angle.

Our first attempt was with Stubby the chipmunk. This little rascal had never shown the least timidity around us. It was not uncommon for him to run all over me, in and out of my pockets, down my neck, or perch on my head. We thought his picture was going to be easy.

Hi-Bub selected a spot where we would have the advantage of sunlight, sat down and began calling, "Here, Stubby, here, Stubby."

Stubby came on the run. When he was within ten feet of the waiting boy he stopped for some reason. He started to chirp, why I do not know. There was nothing new around except the camera, and that wasn't so vicious-looking. We coaxed, we begged, we even threatened a little— but Stubby just crouched inside a shadow and scolded. Hi-Bub offered him peanuts but the chipmunk wouldn't come.

At last, after fifteen minutes of patient pleading, the tiny creature suddenly darted up to Hi-Bub and ran to his shoulder to get a peanut. I hurried back in position with the camera. By the time I had found the small image in the view finder, Stubby had the peanut and dashed away. No picture. We waited fifteen minutes for his return. By this time the sun had moved and a heavy shadow covered the spot we had chosen for the scene.

Next we tried Salt. He came waddling down the path apparently with no ambition or object in life. I picked him up and carried him to a spot of sunshine, figuring it didn't make any difference to him where he was anyway. Hi-Bub knelt beside him and I stepped back to take the scene. Whereupon Salt moved over under some brush and with a heavy sigh lay down. We carried him out again. This time I tried to hold him while Hi-Bub took the picture. Salt wiggled around until his back was toward the camera. I turned him about, getting some of his quills in my hand while doing so. Then I forcefully held him in a fairly favorable position, calling to Hi-Bub to get the picture quickly. First Hi-Bub couldn't find the image in the view finder. Then he couldn't find the thing-amajig to push. By the time he did find it Salt had twisted out of my grasp. Hi-Bub hurriedly snapped the scene. Days later when it came back developed, it showed a blur where Salt should be and my mouth was wide open as if I were trying to bite him.

Next it was Still-Mo. She was much more co-operative. Right into the sunlight she came, jumping to my hand to get the peanuts I offered. The only trouble was the picture had to be snapped at just the right moment or it was lost. The red squirrel wasn't sitting around posing for anyone. It was all business with her. She came to get food. There was just one instant when a picture could be made. That was when she was taking a peanut and fitting it between her teeth. Prior to that, she was coming too fast, after that she was going too fast. Hi-Bub took picture after picture. Fortunately such small film is not expensive. The first picture showed nothing but my hand where Still-Mo had been. The next was a blur made as she dashed away. So was the next and the next. At last, Hi-Bub had taken one that gave promise of being everything we wanted. Still-Mo sat for a moment examining a peanut that had the shell broken, and she was making sure she wanted it. It was a perfect opportunity—only Hi-Bub had forgotten to turn the film after taking the previous scene, and we had a beautiful double exposure.

It took many hours of work before Hi-Bub had his first success. Finally, though, his album held the likenesses of Blooey, Still-Mo, Beggar Boy, Stubby and Salt. There were some pictures of white-throated sparrows, song sparrows, and chickadees too—but they were the kind that needed the comment, "It may not look like it, but that dot on the ground is a bird."

Although the little box camera was hardly suitable for such work, we tried for pictures of shore-line animals anyway. There was an old blue heron who permitted us to get close enough to make a fairly acceptable view. A muskrat swam near our boat and Hi-Bub "shot" him—that is, most of him. The animal's head got out of the picture, though his tail was there and the wake he was making through the water. A frog who was so sleepy he couldn't move anyway made a very good subject.

Most of all Hi-Bub yearned for a picture of Specks. It was like asking for a miracle. Seldom had we seen the beautiful fawn in the daytime, and the few times we had he had been quite shy. Nevertheless we decided we would try to get him.

Early one morning we went out on a trail in the forest where Specks lived. It was a bright morning. The sunshine was streaming through the trees, laying a delicate pattern of shadows on the forest floor. "If we could find Specks in a place like this, Hi-Bub, I believe we could get his picture," I said to the anxious lad.

"Oh boy, oh boy," he exclaimed, fixing his camera all ready for action in the way I had taught him.

"Remember, if you see him, don't hurry," I cautioned. "You must get close to him or it won't be a good picture. Move up slowly and quietly—you know, the way an Indian would do."

"Uh-huh," said Hi-Bub.

We went silently down the trail. The day was filled with autumn splendor. The forest was colorful as a flower garden. Crows and jays were giving their fall cries. Squirrels were scurrying about gathering food. Chickadees talked to us as we moved along.

Then suddenly Hi-Bub stopped and pointed ahead. At the top of a little rise stood a beautiful fawn right in the middle of our trail.

"It's Thpeckth," he said in a whisper, so excited he was lisping extra. "It'th Thpeckth, Tham Cammel."

"Maybe it is," I whispered back. "Looks like him anyway. Easy now—we must get closer. Is your camera all ready?"

Hi-Bub gave it a quick glance. Yes, it was all ready,

the thingamajig in place and everything. Then we moved toward the young deer. He had not discovered us as yet.

Hi-Bub led the way. Really, he did a good job of stalking the animal. He carefully chose his steps so as not to rustle leaves or crack twigs. The fawn was eating something on the ground. Hi-Bub ceased moving whenever the deer's head came up. When he reached down again, the boy took more steps in his direction.

"When you are level with that birch tree ahead, you'll be close enough for the picture," I breathed in the boy's ear, indicating a tree still fifty feet beyond. "Don't get excited. Don't get buck fever the way some hunters do."

"I won't," he said, as he resumed his silent march.

I sank to my knees in a shadow to let Hi-Bub go on alone. It was fun to watch him. There was nothing novice-like in the way he did this. He was steady, cool and thoughtful. Getting this picture was the most important thing in the world for him at the moment. He was determined to do it right.

Now comes the part of this story I do not like to write. It is no doubt an indication of good that we love happy endings and always seek to avoid evil. Intuitively we know that life is meant to be harmonious. Yet in our human mental make-up there are still phases of evil which bring into experience events which hurt and grieve. Because we know they are wrong is evidence that sooner or later we shall correct them. But until we do, our hearts are going to be heavy at times.

Hi-Bub reached the position beside the birch tree. Still the fawn did not see him or else did not feel frightened.

Hi-Bub raised the view finder to his eye. His finger reached for the thingamajig. Then suddenly I heard a little twang—a sound foreign to our woods. Hi-Bub looked up, startled. Something had happened to the fawn. The creature gave a little bleat something like that of a lamb. He whirled and started to run. Then he collapsed into a quivering pathetic little heap, and I saw to my horror that an arrow was buried in his breast.

"Tham Cammel, Tham Cammel, Tham Cammel," cried Hi-Bub in confusion. "What'th happened to Thpeckth, what——" His sentence broke off in a sob.

I hurried to him and whispered in his ear what words of comfort I could think of in the distress of the moment. How I wished I might have saved him from this meeting with the world's rougher ways! Surely I did not expect he would find it in our Sanctuary. I asked him to stay where he was, and rushed over to the wounded fawn. One glance told me there was nothing I could do for the creature.

The hunter who had shot the arrow approached from the opposite direction, bow in hand, a quiver full of arrows on his back. I had a battle with my own thinking as I saw him. He was a robust fellow whom I might have liked to meet in other circumstances. Now, however, resentment and almost hatred were trying to rule my thoughts.

I am not so foolish in my love of nature as to believe hunting should be or could be banished from the whole forest. Wild life, as we know it now, requires this harvesting. Feeding areas are limited and various species might easily increase to a point where they would bring about their own tragedy. Yet hunting should be done with a minimum of cruelty and a maximum of sportsmanship. Certainly there was no semblance of sportsmanship in selecting this innocent fawn as a target.

"You did this?" I asked the man as he neared me.

He nodded his head.

"I'm at a loss to know what to say to you," I declared, striving to keep anger down. "I could have you arrested. You are on my property, which is posted against hunting. You are within a State Game Refuge. Hunting is never permitted here."

The man stared at me in surprise. It was obvious that he did not know he had come over the refuge line.

"You needn't fear. I won't seek your arrest," I continued. "That would not bring back this fawn, nor would it stop the tears of that boy. Regardless of the law, I say you should be ashamed to shoot at a tiny creature like that. He was not over five months old. He still has his baby spots. He was so unafraid he made no effort to run, even with three of us stalking him. If those facts don't make you ashamed, no fine the court could impose would correct you."

These words were uttered in as calm a voice as I could command. I try to school myself not to want revenge but correction in the world. Hi-Bub's unceasing sobs gave a dramatic background to my speech.

The man looked at me without belligerence or challenge. When he spoke his voice was low, his manner humble. "I wonder if you will believe me," he said. "I'm not trying to escape any punishment when I say I am ashamed."

That instant my estimate of the man began to change. It takes courage and character for one to admit he is wrong. It is so much easier to hang doggedly to our mistakes than to correct them. He continued to talk with obvious sincerity.

"I don't know why I did that. Certainly I didn't know I was in a refuge. I'm a stranger in the woods. And I am a beginner with this thing." He indicated the bow he held in his hand. "I really never had the slightest notion I could hit anything I aimed at—I never have before. I saw the fawn and I shot—I don't know why. Believe me when I say I'd give a lot if that arrow had never left my bow."

Now the man looked toward Hi-Bub. "May I speak to him?" he asked. I nodded. "I have one at home about his size," he added, as he went over and knelt beside the heart-broken boy.

It was then that I saw a man punished for an error so severely that it was certain he would never commit the same mistake again. He expressed his sorrow to Hi-Bub. It might have been expected that Hi-Bub would repel him, or cry out against the act in some expression of resentment. Not Hi-Bub, though. The hunter had said, "Sonny, I am sorry, so sorry that if I dared I would be crying the way you are."

Then the boy revealed to me anew the uncomprehended and inexhaustible power of love. To my surprise he whirled about and threw his arms around the hunter. He buried his face in the neck and shoulder of the man and murmured between sobs, "It'th all right, mithter, I gueth you didn't know." He even reached up with his hand and patted the cheek of the hunter to comfort him.

That man would never do such a thing again. He vowed it as he left us, taking his bow and the fawn with him. Hi-Bub had said more to him by his act than I had by my words. The boy had brought into play the highest sense of law. From his own spirit he had spoken to the true self-hood of the hunter, reminding him that kindness and decency are natural to man and that they truly govern the universe.

Hi-Bub needed a lot of mothering and fathering that evening. Giny and I stayed beside his bed until he was sound asleep. He held to our hands tightly, making sure we would not leave him.

"Tham Cammel," he said, his voice softer than usual.

"Yes, little pal."

"I gueth I have to have Little John Deer Foot again." He was very serious.

"Well, I am sure he will come, Hi-Bub," I answered.

"You thee, Little John can help so much," he went on with an occasional sniff thrown in. "He can find Thpeckth' mother and make her happy. Maybe he could find her another baby deer. I gueth I kinda need him."

"I am glad you do, Hi-Bub," I declared. "In truth, to-night I need him too."

XIV

ALWAYS DAWN

HI-BUB's photographic game bag was soon bulging. He caught a picture of Amos, Andy and the Kingfish lined up begging him for food. A game warden who had live-trapped some beavers and was transporting them for release elsewhere paused until the little box camera had recorded their images. The much-wanted picture of a fawn was obtained at a resort where one of the creatures came to the kitchen door daily. Near this place a black bear was snapped too—in the unromantic setting of a garbage pit. It wasn't a very good picture, for the bear was far away and tin cans were scattered about in the foreground. Hi-Bub prized it, though. He had a good view of a skunk. The little striped animal must have had some vanity in him, for he posed perfectly, though Hi-Bub went much closer to him than is generally advisable with such a creature.

He was becoming so adept at handling his simple little camera that already there were plans afoot for getting him a better one.

On the last night before Giny and I departed once again for our winter's work, we held a farewell campfire party at the Sanctuary. The air was frosty, but our fire was large and we huddled close to it. Ada, Ray and June were there. So were Hi-Bub and his parents—and Hobo, too.

Presently someone suggested that we go to the salt lick to see if we could find Specks's mother. We had felt no interest in returning to that spot after the sad experience with the bow-and-arrow hunter. Now time had healed our thoughts somewhat and we went in search of the beautiful doe.

We crossed by boat to the mainland and, flashlights in hand, started down the trail to the salt lick. Hobo, as usual, went bounding far ahead of us, looking for his playmate. There was, of course, no way to tell the dog of our loss.

Hobo immediately found something to excite him, however. Long before we reached the salt lick we heard him racing about yelping in tones that sounded quite happy. We hurried a bit, wondering if he had forgotten the lesson of the pliers and was bothering some wild creature.

When our lights revealed the cause of the sounds, however, we found that Hobo was playing with a fawn! This playmate was chasing him and being chased—just as Specks had often done in the past. The fawn knew just what to do. He was leading the dog over logs and over brush piles, having a wonderful time. Then to our amazement, when Hobo ran up to tell us what fun this was, the fawn came along!

"It'th Thpeckth, Tham Cammel!" cried Hi-Bub. "Thpeckth has come back!"

Sure enough, it was Specks—alive, well, sprightly—

with not so much as a scar on his lovely neck! We all laughed in sheer delight.

Hi-Bub tugged at me until I bent down to hear his whisper.

"Sam Cammel—what was that, you know what I mean—on the trail? Did we just dream it?" he asked seriously.

"Maybe you are right, Hi-Bub, maybe you are right," I whispered back. "Come, let's watch Hobo and Specks— aren't they having fun?"

Back at the campfire our songs were stronger and more joyous that night. A friendship had been saved.

It was time to go and we were ready. The animals of the island were busy with their preparations for winter.

Amos, Andy and the Kingfish were sound asleep in a protected spot under our cabin. Salt was high and happy in a pine tree.

Hi-Bub had so much to think about he was not the least distressed at our departure. A new camera had arrived, and it had so many thingamajigs to push and press he was bewildered. Besides, Giny and I had given him a promise. I spread a map of the Canadian canoe country before him and helped him mentally picture the wilderness lake we had found in that grand country. "Someday we'll take you to that lake, Hi-Bub," I said, and added quickly, "when you are a little older, a little stronger and a little taller."

The prospect fired the ever-ready imagination of our lad. His parents surely wished I had never mentioned the matter. Their house was converted into the Canadian wilderness by Hi-Bub. Rugs were lakes and he paddled across them in canoes which strangely resembled overturned chairs. Floor lamps became pine trees, foot stools were animals, and Hobo kept pace with it all, not knowing just what was going on, but determined not to be left out. A tent was pitched in the parlor, though it took up so much space that Hi-Bub's mother and father could hardly get into the room. At least once a week Hi-Bub's mother had to measure him to see if he was growing. She examined his muscles to see if strength was coming, and she checked months off on a calendar to assure him he was getting older. Hi-Bub was going on a canoe trip—there was no doubt about it.

A pleasing bit of news about Big John Shawano came to us. A young man of Indian blood was coming to live with him for the winter. It would crowd the small cabin, but Big John was more than anxious for his friend to come. This young man could read, and through the long winter months he would reveal to John the sacred contents of his beloved "Big Book."

Giny and I stood taking one last look at the wooded shore lines of our lake before we left.

"What do you suppose the forest will have to offer us in the way of adventure when we return in the spring?" I ventured.

Giny contemplated the green mansions that stretched endlessly into the distance. It was a reservoir of interest and experience which could never be exhausted. Then with wisdom she said, "We shall see the same old wonderful things in a marvelous new way."